Key Stage Two
Maths Investigations
Teacher Book for Year 6

This Teacher Book accompanies CGP's Year 6 Maths Investigations Question Book.

It's matched page-to-page with the Question Book and includes background information to help teachers introduce and teach each investigation. Detailed answers are included too!

We've also made some handy printable resources to go alongside the investigations — you can download them from this page:

www.cgpbooks.co.uk/KS2-Maths-Investigations

Or you can scan this QR code:

Printable Resources

What CGP is all about

Our sole aim here at CGP is to produce the highest quality books — carefully written, immaculately presented and dangerously close to being funny.

Then we work our socks off to get them out to you — at the cheapest possible prices.

Contents

Section One — Calculations

Investigating how to produce a lower answer using multiplication, with the help of a calculator.

- *Prerequisite learning: multiplication using decimals and negative numbers.*

Exploring the binary number system, representing binary numbers in tables and graphically, looking for patterns.

- *Prerequisite learning: speedy mental addition.*
- *Online resource available: squared paper.*

Using knowledge of multiplication and doubling to solve division calculations.

- *Prerequisite learning: multiplication facts up to 12 × 12; ability to use doubling to solve multiplication problems beyond 12 × 12; ability to divide by 1- and 2-digit numbers.*

Changing one aspect (e.g. number or operation) of an equation to make it correct.

- *Prerequisite learning: BIDMAS.*

Section Two — Fractions and Ratios

Using folded paper to visualise fractions of a whole, and fractions of fractions.

- *Prerequisite learning: recognition of visual representations of fractions.*

Exploring the relationship between fractions and decimals by using a calculator to find decimal equivalents.

- *Prerequisite learning: decimal equivalents of common fractions.*

Introducing the concept of ratios, with number rods as a visual aid, and working systematically to find all possible ratios using a given set of rods.

- *Prerequisite learning: equivalent fractions.*
- *Online resource available: printable number rods.*

Contents

Published by CGP

ISBN: 978 1 78908 902 8

Written by Amanda MacNaughton and Mike Ollerton.

Editors: Ellen Burton, Sharon Keeley-Holden, Sam Norman
Reviewer: Clare Selway
With thanks to Glenn Rogers and Caley Simpson for the proofreading.

Printed by Elanders Ltd, Newcastle upon Tyne.
Clipart from Corel®
Based on the classic CGP style created by Richard Parsons.

How To Use This Book

This book guides teachers through each of the investigations in the pupil book. Each page in the pupil book has an accompanying page in the teacher book, as shown below:

The pupil page, with the answers written on in red.

Introduction to the investigation, and list of its aims.

List of key vocabulary, and list of required resources (if any).

Green boxes explain extra support that can be given to struggling pupils.

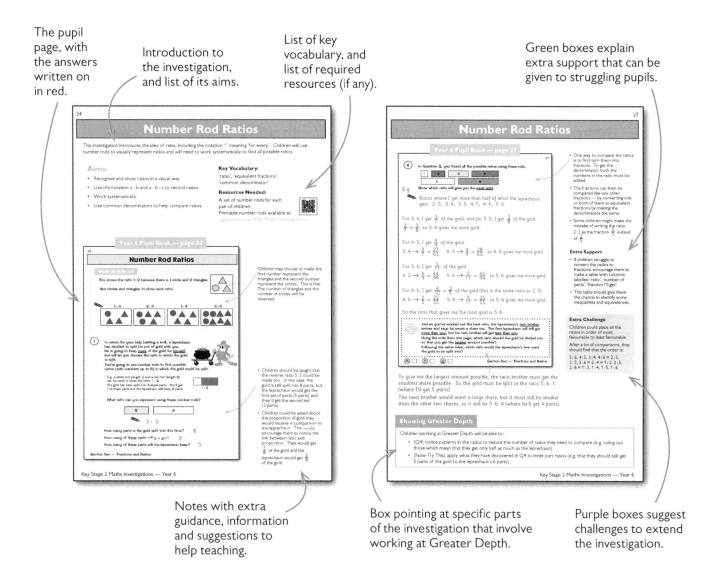

Notes with extra guidance, information and suggestions to help teaching.

Box pointing at specific parts of the investigation that involve working at Greater Depth.

Purple boxes suggest challenges to extend the investigation.

It is a good idea to read through the investigation and teacher notes before delivering each lesson, as this will allow you to prepare, e.g.:

• Required <u>resources</u> — e.g. maths manipulatives or print-outs
  (some investigations have accompanying printable online resources —
  these are found at cgpbooks.co.uk/KS2-Maths-Investigations or by scanning the QR code).

• Any other set-up — e.g. some investigations may require children to work in mixed-ability <u>pairings</u> or <u>groups</u>, and some may benefit from a large <u>space</u> being available.

• <u>Timings</u> — investigations could take varying lengths of time, depending on the learners and environment you are working in. You might need to be prepared with the suggested extra challenges, if you expect some children to finish early.

The next page gives more general advice for leading these investigations.

How To Use This Book

During the Lesson

- There will be many opportunities throughout these investigations to stop the lesson for a <u>mini-plenary</u> or quick class discussion.
- Ask the children what they have found out so far or what they have noticed.
- Ask children to demonstrate how they are being <u>systematic</u>.
- Regularly remind children that good mathematicians <u>test ideas</u> and <u>predictions</u>; they get things wrong sometimes and learn from it.
- Ask children at the end of sessions to talk about the maths skills they have used today.

Greater Depth

Each investigation provides opportunities for children to demonstrate '<u>Greater Depth</u>'.
These require not only mastery of the mathematical concept being taught, but also skills such as:

- <u>analysis</u> (breaking down a problem into its component parts).
- <u>synthesis</u> (bringing different mathematical concepts together).
- <u>metacognition</u> (reflecting on what and how they are learning).
- <u>creativity</u> (transferring their understanding to a new situation).

Skills Needed for Completing Investigations

Maths investigations involve a special set of skills that help children to deal with mathematical situations in real life. They need to:

- <u>work systematically</u> (collect and work out information in an orderly way).
- <u>spot patterns</u> and <u>make predictions</u> (use evidence to decide what will happen next).
- <u>generate rules</u> (use evidence to make generalisations).
- <u>show their thinking</u> (write down their thoughts and findings).

Introduce pupils to these skills using pages 1-2 of the workbook.

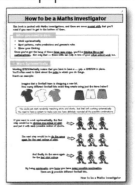
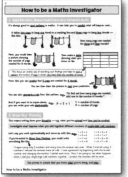

'Showing your thinking' is often called 'Journaling'. It helps children develop their reasoning skills. Thinking more deeply about the maths they are doing will help them to master mathematical concepts and show greater depth in their work.

Talk them through the examples and invite them to think of other examples of where they could apply these skills (e.g. in Science or Computer Science).

Always, Sometimes or Never?

In this investigation, children will be changing an expression in order to make it equal to a particular number. They'll also consider how multiplication can make a number lower. Children should be familiar with using a calculator, and know how to multiply decimals and negative numbers on it.

Aims:

- Vary operations and numbers in equations to get a desired result.
- Know that multiplying a number can make it higher or lower.

Key Vocabulary:

'multiplication', 'decimal places'

Resources Needed:

Calculators

Year 6 Pupil Book — page 3

Section One — Calculations

3

Always, Sometimes or Never?

Warm Up Question

Imagine that some of the keys on a calculator do not work.
How can you make the numbers 1-20 using only the keys below?
Write down the keys you must press in the correct order to get each number.

$$\boxed{\times}\ \boxed{-}\ \boxed{2}\ \boxed{3}\ \boxed{7}\ \boxed{=}$$

E.g.

$3 - 2 = \underline{1}$	$3 \times 3 = \underline{9}$	$2 \times 7 = \underline{14}$
$\underline{2}$	$7 - 2 = 5$	$3 \times 7 - 3 - 3 = \underline{15}$
$\underline{3}$	$\times 2 - \underline{10}$	$3 \times 7 - 3 - 2 = \underline{16}$
$7 - 3 = \underline{4}$		$3 \times 7 - 2 - 2 = \underline{17}$
$7 - 2 = \underline{5}$	$2 \times 7 - 3 = \underline{11}$	
$2 \times 3 = \underline{6}$	$2 \times 3 \times 2 = \underline{12}$	$2 \times 3 \times 3 = \underline{18}$
$\underline{7}$	$7 - 3 = 4$	$3 \times 7 - 2 = \underline{19}$
$7 - 3 = 4$	$\times 2 \times 2 = 16$	$7 - 2 = 5$
$\times 2 = \underline{8}$	$- 3 = \underline{13}$	$\times 2 \times 2 = \underline{20}$

(1) "Multiplying numbers produces a higher number."

Remember to give examples to back up what you say and to make it clearer.

Show your thinking

Is this statement <u>always</u> true, <u>sometimes</u> true or <u>never</u> true? Explain your answer.

E.g.

It is always true because multiplying a number means you have more lots of it.

OR

It is sometimes true because when you multiply a number by something like 5 or 7, the result is higher. But when you multiply it by a decimal like 0.1 or 0.2, the result is lower.

Section One — Calculations

- The law of commutativity means that the order of numbers in the multiplications doesn't change the answer, e.g. $2 \times 3 \times 2 = 3 \times 2 \times 2 = 12$.

- The exact answers children give will differ according to the calculator they're using. A basic calculator will do each step in the order it is input. However, scientific calculators perform operations in the BIDMAS order, meaning that when the subtraction comes before the multiplication, it is necessary to press equals before the multiplication part, e.g. "7 – 2 = × 2 × 2 =". Alternatively, brackets can be input, e.g. "(7 – 2) × 2 × 2 =".

- Some children will think the statement is always true because they are used to multiplying by whole positive numbers (in times tables or short multiplication, etc.), e.g. $7 \times 8 = 56$ or $17 \times 4 = 68$. At this stage it is fine that they think this as this investigation will challenge their belief.

- Multiplying by a fraction or decimal less than one will produce a lower answer, e.g. $7 \times 0.8 = 5.6$ or $7 \times \frac{1}{2} = 3.5$. Also, multiplying a positive number by a negative number will produce a negative answer, which is lower than the positive number, e.g. $7 \times -2 = -14$

Always, Sometimes or Never?

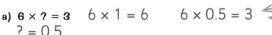
Year 6 Pupil Book — page 4

4

(2) For each calculation below, think about what the <u>missing number</u> might be and write down your suggestion. Then try it out on your <u>calculator</u>. If your number is not correct, <u>try again</u>.

a) **6 × ? = 3** $6 \times 1 = 6$ $6 \times 0.5 = 3$
? = 0.5

b) **5 × ? = 1** $5 \times 0.1 = 0.5$ $5 \times 0.2 = 1$
? = 0.2

c) **10 × ? = 4** $10 \times 0.4 = 4$
? = 0.4

d) **30 × ? = 3** $30 \times 0.1 = 3$
? = 0.1

e) **30 × ? = 12** $30 \times 0.2 = 6$ $30 \times 0.3 = 9$
? = 0.4 $30 \times 0.4 = 12$

f) **3 × ? = –6** $3 \times 2 = 6$ $3 \times 0.2 = 0.6$
? = –2 $3 \times -2 = -6$

g) **4 × ? = –12** $4 \times 0.3 = 1.2$ $4 \times -3 = -12$
? = –3

h) **10 × ? = –3** $10 \times -0.3 = -3$
? = –0.3

i) **0.5 × ? = 0.25** $0.5 \times 5 = 2.5$
? = 0.5 $0.5 \times 0.5 = 0.25$

j) **0.1 × ? = 0.01** $0.1 \times 0.1 = 0.01$
? = 0.1

> Trial and Improvement is when you begin with one number, try it out and adjust it until you get to the right answer.

Section One — Calculations

One way of looking at it is to see the fraction relationship between the two numbers, e.g.
3 is $\frac{1}{2}$ of 6 and $\frac{1}{2}$ as a decimal is 0.5. Similarly, 1 is $\frac{1}{5}$ of 5 and $\frac{1}{5}$ is written as 0.2.

Extra Support

If children are struggling, model how they could use trial and improvement to find the answer.
E.g. $6 \times 1 = 6$ (so the ? must be less than 1)
     $6 \times 0.5 = 3$

Extra Support

Prompt children to think about how they would get an answer 10 times bigger than the one they're trying to get to.
E.g. If this was $10 \times ? = 40$, they'll know the ? = 4.
To get an answer that is 10 times smaller, the ? must also be 10 smaller, so ? = 0.4.

These missing numbers could also be written as fractions. (They haven't been so that the calculations can be checked easily with a basic calculator.)

Extra Support

Some children may need help to see that when the answer is negative the ? must be negative.

One way to explain this is to talk about walking along a number line.
E.g. $4 \times 3 = 12$ can be modelled by walking 4 lots of 3 steps along a number line in the forwards direction. This gets you to 12.

To get to –12, you can do 4 lots of 3 steps in the reverse direction, which is 4×-3.

Always, Sometimes or Never?

5

Show your thinking

"Multiplying numbers produces a higher number."
Is there anything you would change or add to your original thinking?

 E.g. When the original number is positive:

- Multiplying by a decimal number less than 1 makes the answer lower, e.g. 6 × 0.5 = 3.
- Multiplying by a negative number also gives a lower answer, e.g. 6 × –5 = –30.

What children write depends on what they wrote earlier in the investigation. If children hadn't previously recognised that multiplication doesn't always produce a higher number, they should do so now.

(3) Find as many <u>multiplications</u> as you can which have an answer with exactly <u>2 decimal places</u> which is between <u>0 and 1</u>.

Here's an example for you:
0.5 × 0.3 = 0.15

You can't include 0.5 × 0.2 because the answer is 0.1, which only has 1 decimal place. Writing it as 0.10 isn't allowed!

 E.g.

0.2 × 0.1 = 0.02	2 × 0.01 = 0.02
0.3 × 0.4 = 0.12	3 × 0.04 = 0.12
0.4 × 0.4 = 0.16	4 × 0.04 = 0.16
0.2 × 0.2 = 0.04	2 × 0.02 = 0.04
0.3 × 0.5 = 0.15	3 × 0.05 = 0.15
0.4 × 0.6 = 0.24	4 × 0.06 = 0.24

Extra Support

Less confident children could use the example given to base additional calculations on.

- Note that a number with 2 decimal places must have 2 digits after the decimal point. Therefore, 0.4 × 0.5 = 0.2 does not count as the 0 that would be in the hundredths column is redundant. However, 0.2 × 0.1 = 0.02 does count as the 0 in the tenths column is necessary.

 10 × __ = __ × 0.5
There are two missing numbers in this equation. Each number can be whole, a decimal or a fraction, and positive or negative. Investigate how many different ways you could complete this equation.

Section One — Calculations

- To be systematic, children might keep one number the same and change the other number each time (rather like in times tables).

- Some children might think that 0.2 × 0.2 = 0.4. Address this common misconception by rewriting the calculation as 2 ÷ 10 × 2 ÷ 10 = 4 ÷ 10 ÷ 10 = 0.4 ÷ 10 = 0.04.

- Children could check their own calculations (or their partner's) using a calculator.

E.g. 10 × 2 = 40 × 0.5
10 × 0.3 = 6 × 0.5
10 × –4 = –80 × 0.5

Showing Greater Depth

Children working at Greater Depth will be able to:

- (Q2 'Show Your Thinking') explain that multiplying by a number less than one or by a negative number will result in a product lower than the original number.

- (Now Try This) identify the relationship between the two missing numbers in order to quickly generate pairs of values. (The right-hand value is 20 times the left-hand value.)

Binary Numbers

In this investigation, children will explore the binary number system. They'll use 'binary headings' to make a variety of totals in a grid and look for patterns in their work. For this investigation, children need to add mentally with speed and accuracy.

Aims:

- Understand that different number systems exist.
- Develop knowledge of the binary number system.
- Make a given total by adding selected numbers from a set.
- Look for patterns in their work.

Key Vocabulary:

'binary number'

Resources Needed:

Squared paper
Printable squared paper available at:
cgpbooks.co.uk/KS2-Maths-Investigations

Year 6 Pupil Book — page 6

6

Binary Numbers

Warm Up Questions

Make the totals below by **adding** numbers from the cards on the right. You can only use each card **once** in a sum.

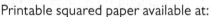 **1 2 4 8 16**

1) 9   8 + 1

2) 14   8 + 4 + 2

3) 21   16 + 4 + 1

① Can **all** the totals from 1 to 31 be made using the cards above? Show your working.

Yes.

1: 1
2: 2
3: 2 + 1
4: 4
5: 4 + 1
6: 4 + 2
7: 4 + 2 + 1
8: 8
9: 8 + 1
10: 8 + 2
11: 8 + 2 + 1
12: 8 + 4
13: 8 + 4 + 1

14: 8 + 4 + 2
15: 8 + 4 + 2 + 1
16: 16
17: 16 + 1
18: 16 + 2
19: 16 + 2 + 1
20: 16 + 4
21: 16 + 4 + 1
22: 16 + 4 + 2
23: 16 + 4 + 2 + 1
24: 16 + 8
25: 16 + 8 + 1
26: 16 + 8 + 2

27: 16 + 8 + 2 + 1
28: 16 + 8 + 4
29: 16 + 8 + 4 + 1
30: 16 + 8 + 4 + 2
31: 16 + 8 + 4 + 2 + 1

> 31 is the biggest number that can be made with these cards.

Section One — Calculations

Extra Support

If children struggle to understand, demonstrate making 9 by asking,

'Do we need 16 to make 9?'
'No.'

'Do we need 8 to make 9?'
'Yes.'

'Do we need 4?'
'No.'

'Do we need 2?'
'No.'

'Do we need 1?'
'Yes, because 8 + 1 = 9.''

Encourage children to select the numbers needed starting with the largest (16), then working through to the smallest (1).

Binary Numbers

7

(2) The chart below shows how the numbers from 1 to 5 can be made using <u>binary column headings</u> and only the <u>digits 0 and 1</u>. Complete the table to show how the numbers 6 to 16 can be made.

16	8	4	2	1	
				1	= 1
			1	0	= 2
			1	1	= 3
		1	0	0	– 4
		1	0	1	= 5
		1	1	0	= 6
		1	1	1	= 7
	1	0	0	0	= 8
	1	0	0	1	= 9
	1	0	1	0	= 10
	1	0	1	1	= 11
	1	1	0	0	= 12
	1	1	0	1	= 13
	1	1	1	0	= 14
	1	1	1	1	= 15
1	0	0	0	0	= 16

What <u>patterns</u> do you notice in the table?

E.g. Odd numbers end in 1 and even numbers end in 0.
In the column with 2 as its heading, the pattern
goes 1 1 0 0 1 1 0 0.
In the column with 4 as its heading, the pattern goes
1 1 1 1 0 0 0 0 1 1 1 1.

Section One — Calculations

- Children might need the relationship between the work they did on the previous page and this chart explaining to them.

- It might not seem important to include the zeros at the moment, but they will become necessary on the next page.

- Children could be asked to predict what the patterns in the '8' column and the '16' column will be. They should then test whether they are correct.

- Children could also use the patterns they have noticed to write the next several lines in the table. Again, they should add along the rows to check their patterns do continue.

Dec means 10.
Bi means 2.

- Binary is a base-2 number system — there are only two digits involved: 0 and 1. The decimal number system is base-10 — there are ten digits involved: 0, 1, 2, 3, 4, 5, 6, 7, 8 and 9.

- When counting up in the decimal system, we first go through the digits 0 to 9, then go back to 0, putting a 1 in the column on the left, which is then increased by 1 each time. When counting in the binary system, it is the same, but there are only two digits, so we count through 0 and 1, then return to 0, adding 1s to the columns on the left.

- Binary is used by computers, as it means they can use 'on' and 'off' signals to represent numbers. 'On' (or high voltage) is usually 1, and 'off' (or low voltage) is usually 0.

Binary Numbers

8

(3) We can use the table to help us write numbers as <u>binary numbers</u>.
E.g. 5 = 1 0 1, 13 = 1 1 0 1. More rows could be added to the table to help us write the numbers up to 31 as binary numbers.

Complete the table and use it to write the numbers as binary numbers.

16	8	4	2	1	
1	0	1	1	0	= 22
1	1	0	1	1	= 27
1	1	1	0	0	= 28
1	1	1	1	1	= 31

22   1 0 1 1 0   27   1 1 0 1 1

28   1 1 1 0 0   31   1 1 1 1 1

Emphasise the importance of including a zero as a 'place holder' where a number isn't used. The zeros help to give the 1s the correct values, as this depends on which columns they are in (just like in the decimal system).

Show your thinking

This table can only record numbers up to 31 using the digits 0 and 1. How could the table be changed so that numbers <u>bigger than 31</u> can be recorded using the digits 0 and 1? HINT: look at the pattern in the column headings.

Extra columns should be added on the left. Each column heading is double the one to the right of it, so the heading of the next column should be 32 (16 × 2), then the next 64 (32 × 2).

Some children will be able to apply what they have discovered so far to find the highest possible total with one new column. (It's 63: 32 + 16 + 8 + 4 + 2 + 1)

(4) Write the following as <u>binary numbers</u>. You might need to draw a table.

64	32	16	8	4	2	1
36		1	0	0	1	0	0
60		1	1	1	1	0	0
75	1	0	0	1	0	1	1

36   1 0 0 1 0 0

60   1 1 1 1 0 0

75   1 0 0 1 0 1 1

To find the binary number for 75, children will need to realise that an additional column with a heading of 64 is required.

Section One — Calculations

Extra Challenge

Ask the children if they can see a pattern with the greatest heading number and the maximum total that can be made.

They may recognise that the maximum is one less than double the greatest heading.

Greatest Heading	Maximum total
16	31
32	63
64	127

Alternatively, they could look for the link between the number of columns and the maximum total.

Number of columns	Maximum total	
5	31	$= 2^5 - 1$
6	63	$= 2^6 - 1$
7	127	$= 2^7 - 1$

Binary Numbers

9

5 An alternative to using 1s and 0s is to use a <u>shaded square</u> to represent <u>1</u> and an <u>unshaded square</u> to represent <u>0</u>.

You can create <u>binary monsters</u> from the patterns created. The monster below can be described using the code: 17, 21, 27, 14, 14, 10, 27

Complete the binary monster using the totals at the ends of the rows.

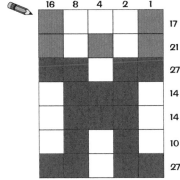

Extra Support

It might help children to place 1 or 0 in each square (to create the binary number) before shading in the squares.

6 You are going to create your own binary monster. First shade the squares to make your monster, then write the totals at the end of the rows.

E.g.

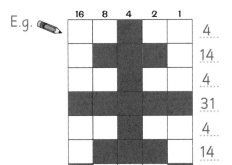

What is the binary code for your monster?

4, 14, 4, 31, 4, 14, 17

Children could use each other's codes to draw their monster. This will act as a check that codes are accurate.

> **Now Try This**
> Take the binary code for your monster and <u>double</u> each number in it.
> Redraw the monster on to a new grid (you may need to add a column).
> What changes do you notice about the monster?

This could be called a 'Lefty Monster'. Ask children how they could create a 'Righty Monster'. (They'll need to halve the numbers in the binary code, which presents a problem with odd numbers.)

Section One — Calculations

E.g. Doubled binary code = 8, 28, 8, 62, 8, 28, 34

The monster has not changed in shape or size but it has moved across one column to the left.

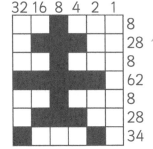

Showing Greater Depth

Children working at Greater Depth will be able to:

- (Q4) identify the relationships between the maximum totals and the greatest heading/number of columns (see the teacher's notes on the previous page).

- (Now Try This) explain why the monster moves one place to the left. (It is because the headings are doubling each time so doubling the number just moves everything one place to the left. This can be related to the decimal system — when numbers are multiplied by 10, digits move one place to the left.)

Division and Doubling

In this investigation, children will work in pairs to use their knowledge of multiplication and doubling to solve division calculations. In order to tackle the investigation, children should know multiplication facts to 12 × 12 and be able to use doubling to find derivatives of these.

Aims:

- Perform mental addition calculations.

- Use a formal method to divide numbers by 1- or 2-digit numbers.

- Notice patterns in their work.

Key Vocabulary:

'multiples'

Resources Needed:

Colouring pencils

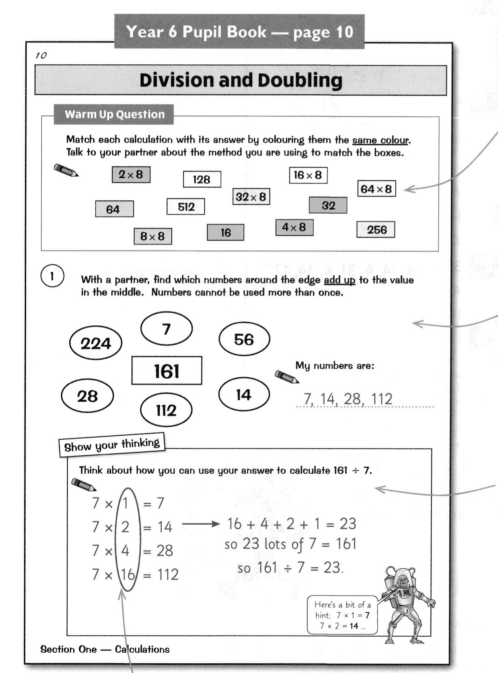

Children need to recognise that each calculation is doubling in size and therefore so is the answer. Point out that once you have established the answer to the smallest calculation, you just need to use doubling to solve the remaining calculations.

- Encourage children to notice that, in all of these questions, the numbers around the outside can be obtained by starting with the smallest and successively doubling.

- Encourage children to work systematically to find the numbers that add up to make the required total.

- They should begin with the largest number first, i.e. 112 (because 224 is too big) then add 28 (because 112 + 56 is too big) then add 14, then 7.

Children need to understand that each of the numbers around the outside is a multiple or 'lot' of 7. How many lots of 7 there are is the answer to the division.

The answer can be checked with a formal method:

$$7\overline{\smash{)}16^21}\;\;^{23}$$

The circled numbers show the 'lots of 7' needed to make 161. Children can see that 16 lots of 7 is 112 if they think about the numbers in the question being successively doubled — they know 8 lots of 7 is 56, so double that is 16 lots of 7 = 112.

Division and Doubling

Again, make sure children are calculating the total by starting with the largest possible number first — they should work out that 288 + 36 + 18 = 342.

② Use the numbers below (as well as what you and your partner think is going on in Question 1) to calculate 342 ÷ 9.

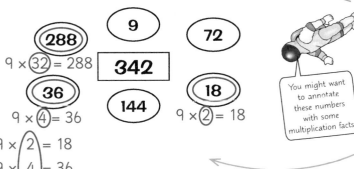

9 × ㉜ = 288

342

9 × ④ = 36

9 × ② = 18

$9 \times 2 = 18$
$9 \times 4 = 36$
$9 \times 32 = 288$ ⟶ 32 + 4 + 2 = 38
38 lots of 9 = 342

342 ÷ 9 = ..38..

You might want to annotate these numbers with some multiplication facts.

- Pupils should realise that all the numbers are multiples of 9, and write these multiplication facts for the required three.

- To work out 288 ÷ 9, encourage pupils to use doubling, i.e. 9, 18, 36, 72, 144, 288. This should lead them to see that 288 is 32 lots of 9.

- The 'lots of 9' are added together to get the final answer.

③ Now have a go at 473 ÷ 11.

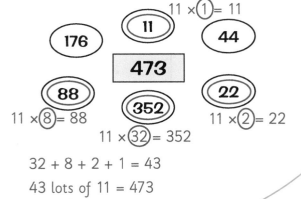

11 × ① = 11

11 × ⑧ = 88

11 × ㉜ = 352

11 × ② = 22

32 + 8 + 2 + 1 = 43
43 lots of 11 = 473

473 ÷ 11 = ..43..

Section One — Calculations

- Again, this answer can be checked with a formal method:

$$11\overline{)47^3{}3}$$
$$43$$

- Children could use a longer, 'chunking' method to check this division as they are dividing by a 2-digit number:

```
        43
   11 ) 473
      - 440   (40 × 11)
        33
      -  33   (3 × 11)
         0
```

- Discuss the importance of checking answers using a different method.

If children struggle to use the method, encourage them to practise using smaller numbers.
E.g. calculate 90 ÷ 9 using the method:

⑨ |90| ⑱

㉒   ㊱

72 + 18 = 90 → 9 × 8 = 72
                  9 × 2 = 18

8 + 2 = 10 lots of 9 = 90,
so 90 ÷ 9 = 10

Or, calculate 44 ÷ 4 using the method

④ |44| ⑧

㉜   ⑯

32 + 8 + 4 = 44 → 4 × 8 = 32
                     4 × 2 = 8
                     4 × 1 = 4

8 + 2 + 1 = 11 lots of 4 = 44,
so 44 ÷ 4 = 11

Division and Doubling

12

4 Yep, you're an expert now... See if you and your partner can use some of the numbers below to help you work out 527 ÷ 17.

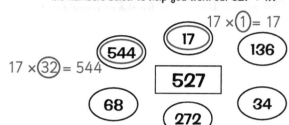

$17 \times \textcircled{1} = 17$

$17 \times \textcircled{32} = 544$

527

544 − 17 = 527

32 − 1 = 31

31 lots of 17 = 527

527 ÷ 17 = _31_

- Encourage children to use 544, i.e. 544 − 17 = 527, rather than adding all the other numbers together.

- This should lead them to work out that 527 is 32 lots of 17 minus 1 lot of 17, i.e. 31 lots of 17.

- Their written calculations may begin to look more compact as they become more familiar with the method.

5 There's some extra work to be done here to calculate 315 ÷ 21.

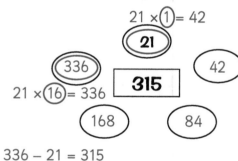

$21 \times \textcircled{1} = 42$

$21 \times \textcircled{16} = 336$

315

336 − 21 = 315

16 − 1 = 15

15 lots of 21 = 315

315 ÷ 21 = _15_

- Children should have noticed that the numbers in the ovals in other questions have all been doubles, so they should use these blank ovals to keep doubling, starting with 21.

- Using the same method as in Question 4, children can just subtract 21 from 336 to get the target number. However, they might add together 21, 42, 84 and 168 instead. This will lead them to add together the 'lots of' 21, i.e. 8 + 4 + 2 + 1 = 15.

Section One — Calculations

Division and Doubling

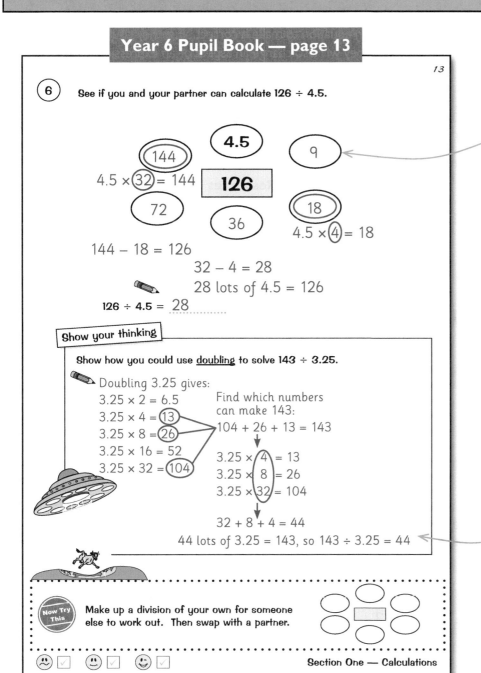

13

6 See if you and your partner can calculate 126 ÷ 4.5.

(144) **4.5** (9)

$4.5 \times \textcircled{32} = 144$ **126**

(72) (36) (18)

$4.5 \times \textcircled{4} = 18$

$144 - 18 = 126$

$32 - 4 = 28$

28 lots of 4.5 = 126

$126 \div 4.5 = \underline{28}$

Show your thinking

Show how you could use <u>doubling</u> to solve 143 ÷ 3.25.

Doubling 3.25 gives:

$3.25 \times 2 = 6.5$ Find which numbers
$3.25 \times 4 = \textcircled{13}$ can make 143:
$3.25 \times 8 = \textcircled{26}$ 104 + 26 + 13 = 143
$3.25 \times 16 = 52$
$3.25 \times 32 = \textcircled{104}$

$3.25 \times \textcircled{4} = 13$
$3.25 \times \textcircled{8} = 26$
$3.25 \times \textcircled{32} = 104$

$32 + 8 + 4 = 44$

44 lots of 3.25 = 143, so 143 ÷ 3.25 = 44

Now Try This Make up a division of your own for someone else to work out. Then swap with a partner.

Children might be put off by the decimal number, but they should soon realise that it is easy to double, and then they are into familiar territory.

- Even if children are confident with this method now, you can encourage them to continue checking their work by using a more formal method.

- The method they use depends on which they've been taught, and their personal preference.

Showing Greater Depth

Children working at Greater Depth will be able to:

- (Q6 'Show Your Thinking') explain the steps of a method in such a way that someone else could follow them.

- (Now Try This) independently apply their understanding of the method in order to generate a division problem that can be solved in this way.

Change One Aspect

In this investigation, children will change an aspect of an equation to make it correct. E.g. they could change an operation or a number, or they could add brackets. They will also change an aspect of an expression in order to change its value. Children need to be familiar with BIDMAS (or BODMAS) and be able to use it.

Aims:

- Recall what BIDMAS means and how to use it correctly.
- Balance equations by changing an operation or a number.
- Use brackets correctly.
- Work systematically.

Key Vocabulary:

'BIDMAS'

Resources Needed:

None

Year 6 Pupil Book — page 14

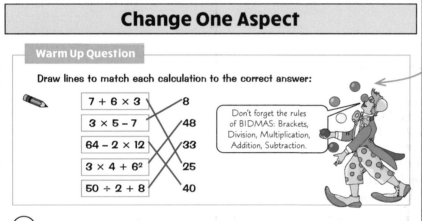

14

Change One Aspect

Warm Up Question

Draw lines to match each calculation to the correct answer:

$7 + 6 \times 3$ 8

$3 \times 5 - 7$ 48

$64 - 2 \times 12$ 33

$3 \times 4 + 6^2$ 25

$50 \div 2 + 8$ 40

Don't forget the rules of BIDMAS: Brackets, Division, Multiplication, Addition, Subtraction.

(1) This equation is <u>incorrect</u>: $7 + 8 = 12$

You are allowed to change <u>one thing</u> to make the equation correct, e.g.

Change the 7 to 4: $4 + 8 = 12$

What else could you change?

E.g. Change the 8 to 5: $7 + 5 = 12$

(2) This equation is incorrect: $25 - 13 = 18$.

Change one thing to make it correct.

E.g. Change the 25 to 31: $31 - 13 = 18$

What else could you change?

Change the 13 to 7: $25 - 7 = 18$

Change the 18 to 12: $25 - 13 = 12$

Section One — Calculations

Before beginning the warm up, children will probably need reminding about the rules of BIDMAS, and the reason they are needed.

E.g. $7 + 6 \times 3$:
$7 + 6 = 13$, $13 \times 3 = 39$
OR $6 \times 3 = 18$, $7 + 18 = 25$.
Only one answer can be correct, but which is it?
BIDMAS tells us to Multiply before Adding, so the second version with an answer of 25 is correct. (If you wanted the expression to equal 39, you'd need to add brackets:
$(7 + 6) \times 3 = 39$.)

Discuss different possibilities with the children. (The 12 could also be changed to 15 to make the equation correct.)

If only one thing is allowed to be changed, the two equations on this page can only be made correct by changing a number.

If you changed a sign you would also have to change a number.

Change One Aspect

15

3 Now you're going to look at a <u>two-step calculation</u> which is incorrect:
$$30 + 10 \times 2 = 10$$
Change <u>one number</u> in this equation to make it correct.

E.g. Change the 10 to 50:
$$30 + 10 \times 2 = 30 + 20 = 50$$

Now change a **different aspect** of the equation (not a number) to make it correct.

You could change an operation (such as multiplication to division) or add brackets.

Remember BIDMAS in this one.

Change the + to −:
$$30 - 10 \times 2 = 30 - 20 = 10$$

4 This equation is <u>incorrect</u>: $5 + 6 \times 3 - 8 = 25$
Change <u>different aspects</u> of the equation one at a time.
How many different aspects can you change to make the equation correct?

E.g. Change 5 to 15: $\mathbf{15} + 6 \times 3 - 8 = 25$ ✓
Change 3 to 5: $5 + 6 \times \mathbf{5} - 8 = 27$ ✗
Change 6 to 9: $5 + \mathbf{9} \times 3 - 8 = 24$ ✗
Change 25 to 15: $5 + 6 \times 3 - 8 = \mathbf{15}$ ✓

Change + to −: $5 - 6 \times 3 - 8 = -21$ ✗
Change × to ÷: $5 + 6 \div 3 - 8 = -1$ ✗
Change − to +: $5 + 6 \times 3 \mathbf{+} 8 = 31$ ✗

Add brackets around the addition:
$$(5 + 6) \times 3 - 8 = 25 ✓$$
Add brackets around the subtraction:
$$5 + 6 \times (3 - 8) = -25 ✗$$

Section One — Calculations

- If children suggest changing the 10 to 80, they will need reminding that because of BIDMAS they should do the multiplication first to get 20 and then add 30.

- Children who are comfortable working with negative numbers might suggest changing the 30 to −10.

- More able children might notice that the 2 could be changed to −2, which would also create 30 − 20:
  $$30 + 10 \times -2 = 10.$$
  Changing the first 10 to −10 would also have this effect.

- Encourage the children to annotate their equations to show which aspect they have changed.

- Children can either write '25' for each 'answer' to show they haven't changed that aspect of the equation, and then put a cross next to the incorrect equations, or they can write the actual 'answer' that is produced — if this isn't 25, it proves that the equation is incorrect.

- 8 could be changed to −2:
  $$5 + 6 \times 3 - (-2) = 25 ✓$$
  However, this requires children to be very confident with negative numbers.

- Children should be encouraged to use strategies to decide what to change the numbers on the left-hand side of the equation to. E.g. the multiplication in the centre of the left-hand side of the equation must equal 28 if the equation is to be made correct. This is because it has 5 added to it and then 8 subtracted from it: $5 + (28) - 8 = 25$. Neither 6 nor 3 are factors of 28, so neither of these numbers can be changed to make the equation correct.

Change One Aspect

16

⑤ 7 + 2 × 5 – 2 = a whole number between 11 and 20.
How many ways can you change one aspect of this equation so that it is still <u>true</u>? Write all the possibilities you can find below.

The circles show the parts of each equation that have been systematically changed.

7 + 2 × 5 – 2 = 15
7 + 2 × (5 – 2) = 13
7 + 2 ⊕ 5 – 2 = 12
7 + 2 × 5 ⊕ 2 = 19
7 + 2 × 5 ⊘ 2 = 12

③ + 2 × 5 – 2 = 11
④ + 2 × 5 – 2 = 12
⑤ + 2 × 5 – 2 = 13
⑥ + 2 × 5 – 2 = 14
⑧ + 2 × 5 – 2 = 16
⑨ + 2 × 5 – 2 = 17
⑩ + 2 × 5 – 2 = 18
⑪ + 2 × 5 – 2 = 19
⑫ + 2 × 5 – 2 = 20
7 + ③ × 5 – 2 = 20
7 + 2 × ③ – 2 = 11
7 + 2 × ④ – 2 = 13
7 + 2 × ⑥ – 2 = 17
7 + 2 × ⑦ – 2 = 19
7 + 2 × 5 – ⓪ = 17
7 + 2 × 5 – ① = 16
7 + 2 × 5 – ③ = 14
7 + 2 × 5 – ④ = 13
7 + 2 × 5 – ⑤ = 12
7 + 2 × 5 – ⑥ = 11

Remember to be systematic in your working.

You could also change the last number to –1, –2 or –3.

Extra Challenge

- Children who manage this task easily could be asked to use the digits 5, 3, 9 and 2 to create their own calculation using different operations (×, ÷, +, –). They should then change one aspect at a time and see how many different answers they can make.

- Children could set their own constraints to the challenge. E.g. the answer must be a whole number less than 20.

Now Try This Caleen Calculator says that by adding brackets to the calculation 7 + 3 × 8 – 5, she can create 4 different answers.
Do you agree with her? Explain your reasoning.

Section One — Calculations

Caleen Calculator is correct:

Brackets at the start: (7 + 3) × 8 – 5 = 75
Brackets in the middle: 7 + (3 × 8) – 5 = 26
Brackets at the end: 7 + 3 × (8 – 5) = 16
2 pairs of brackets: (7 + 3) × (8 – 5) = 30

Showing Greater Depth

Children working at Greater Depth will be able to:

- (Q4) explain to others why the numbers 6 and 3 cannot be changed independently, and the equation still be true. They should also be able to suggest pairs of values that could be used if two values were allowed to be changed (factor pairs of 28, e.g. 1 and 28, 2 and 14, or 4 and 7).

- (Q5) determine the minimum and maximum values each number in the equation could be changed to in order for it to remain true. E.g. 7 can be changed to x, where 3 ≤ x ≤ 12.

Multiplying Fractions

Children need to know that multiplying together fractions that are smaller than 1 gives a product smaller than the original fractions (and recognise that this is proof that multiplication does not always create a bigger answer). They'll be dividing paper into unit fractions to show what happens visually when you multiply fractions. They'll learn that a multiplication like $\frac{1}{4} \times$ ___ is the same as saying $\frac{1}{4}$ of ___.

Aims:

- Understand what multiplying by a fraction means.

- Show a visual representation of multiplying fractions.

- Create a rule/formula for multiplying fractions.

Key Vocabulary:

'fractions', 'numerator', 'denominator'

Resources Needed:

Spare pieces of A5 paper.

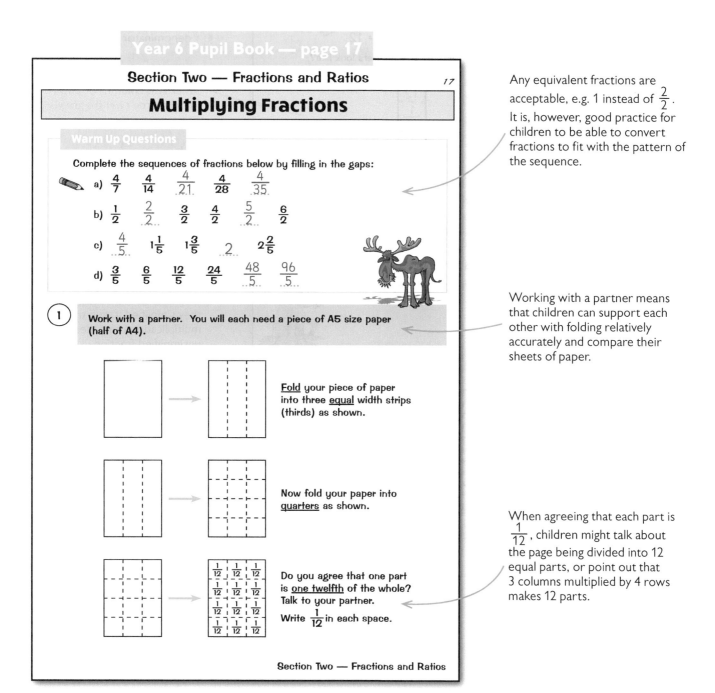

Year 6 Pupil Book — page 17

Section Two — Fractions and Ratios
17

Multiplying Fractions

Warm Up Questions

Complete the sequences of fractions below by filling in the gaps:

a) $\frac{4}{7}$ $\frac{4}{14}$ $\frac{4}{21}$ $\frac{4}{28}$ $\frac{4}{35}$

b) $\frac{1}{2}$ $\frac{2}{2}$ $\frac{3}{2}$ $\frac{4}{2}$ $\frac{5}{2}$ $\frac{6}{2}$

c) $\frac{4}{5}$ $1\frac{1}{5}$ $1\frac{3}{5}$ 2 $2\frac{2}{5}$

d) $\frac{3}{5}$ $\frac{6}{5}$ $\frac{12}{5}$ $\frac{24}{5}$ $\frac{48}{5}$ $\frac{96}{5}$

1 Work with a partner. You will each need a piece of A5 size paper (half of A4).

Fold your piece of paper into three equal width strips (thirds) as shown.

Now fold your paper into quarters as shown.

Do you agree that one part is one twelfth of the whole? Talk to your partner.

Write $\frac{1}{12}$ in each space.

$\frac{1}{12}$ $\frac{1}{12}$ $\frac{1}{12}$
$\frac{1}{12}$ $\frac{1}{12}$ $\frac{1}{12}$
$\frac{1}{12}$ $\frac{1}{12}$ $\frac{1}{12}$
$\frac{1}{12}$ $\frac{1}{12}$ $\frac{1}{12}$

Section Two — Fractions and Ratios

Any equivalent fractions are acceptable, e.g. 1 instead of $\frac{2}{2}$. It is, however, good practice for children to be able to convert fractions to fit with the pattern of the sequence.

Working with a partner means that children can support each other with folding relatively accurately and compare their sheets of paper.

When agreeing that each part is $\frac{1}{12}$, children might talk about the page being divided into 12 equal parts, or point out that 3 columns multiplied by 4 rows makes 12 parts.

Multiplying Fractions

18

2 Fold your piece of paper to show $\frac{3}{4}$ of 1 whole:

$\frac{1}{12}$	$\frac{1}{12}$	$\frac{1}{12}$
$\frac{1}{12}$	$\frac{1}{12}$	$\frac{1}{12}$
$\frac{1}{12}$	$\frac{1}{12}$	$\frac{1}{12}$

So $\frac{3}{4} = \frac{9}{12}$

Using your paper, what does one third of three quarters look like?
Draw it below:

| $\frac{1}{12}$ | $\frac{1}{12}$ | $\frac{1}{12}$ |

OR

So $\frac{1}{3}$ of $\frac{3}{4} = \frac{3}{12}$

This can also be written as $\frac{1}{3} \times \frac{3}{4} = \frac{3}{12}$.

Look at the fraction calculation carefully. If you were to make a
rule for multiplying fractions, what would it be? Write it below.

Multiply the numerators together and
then multiply the denominators together.

3 With a new piece of paper, fold it into 4 columns, then fold it into 5 rows.
Draw what it looks like below.

$\frac{1}{20}$	$\frac{1}{20}$	$\frac{1}{20}$	$\frac{1}{20}$
$\frac{1}{20}$	$\frac{1}{20}$	$\frac{1}{20}$	$\frac{1}{20}$
$\frac{1}{20}$	$\frac{1}{20}$	$\frac{1}{20}$	$\frac{1}{20}$
$\frac{1}{20}$	$\frac{1}{20}$	$\frac{1}{20}$	$\frac{1}{20}$
$\frac{1}{20}$	$\frac{1}{20}$	$\frac{1}{20}$	$\frac{1}{20}$

What is each part worth?
Write the fraction in
each section.

Section Two — Fractions and Ratios

Children should fold back one
row so it can no longer be seen.

Extra Support

If children are stuck here,
tell them that the
denominator is 12.

Here, they should fold away
either two columns or two rows,
so only three twelfths are visible.

Some children may choose
to simplify $\frac{3}{12}$ to $\frac{1}{4}$.

If they have simplified to $\frac{1}{4}$, they
might not come up with a correct
rule here. Encourage them to
look back at the fraction before
they simplified it, and try the
multiplication using the
unsimplified fraction.

Multiplying Fractions

Answers will vary according to the multiplications they choose. Each multiplication should consist of a quarter fraction ($\frac{1}{4}$, $\frac{2}{4}$ or $\frac{3}{4}$) multiplied by a fifth fraction ($\frac{1}{5}$, $\frac{2}{5}$, $\frac{3}{5}$ or $\frac{4}{5}$) so a possible 12 different multiplications.

19

Using fifths (from 5 rows) and quarters (from 4 columns), use your paper to solve different multiplications of fractions, e.g. $\frac{1}{4}$ of $\frac{3}{5}$ or $\frac{2}{5}$ of $\frac{3}{4}$. Record your workings below.

E.g.

It might help to fold your paper to show what each step looks like before writing the multiplication and its answer.

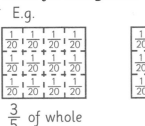

$\frac{3}{5}$ of whole

$\frac{1}{4}$ of $\frac{3}{5}$ = $\frac{3}{20}$

OR $\frac{1}{4}$ × $\frac{3}{5}$ = $\frac{3}{20}$

Extra Support

Children will recognise that $\frac{1}{20}$ comes from there being 4 columns and 5 rows (4 x 5 = 20). Children may need help to realise that to find $\frac{1}{4}$ of $\frac{3}{5}$, they will need to show $\frac{3}{5}$ of the whole thing FIRST.

④ Repeat question 3 choosing any number of columns and rows (make sure you choose numbers you can fold the paper into). Show your workings and findings below. Try to find as many of the possible multiplications as you can.

Answers will vary. E.g.

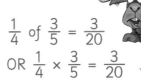

$\frac{2}{5}$ of whole

$\frac{2}{3}$ of $\frac{2}{5}$ = $\frac{4}{15}$

OR $\frac{2}{3}$ × $\frac{2}{5}$ = $\frac{4}{15}$

- This could be an opportunity to differentiate the children's working by allocating them particular denominations.

- Encourage children to find all the different possibilities for the 2 denominations they have chosen, e.g. eighths and thirds will produce 14 different multiplications.

- More able children may choose to apply their rule to the questions and begin not to use the visual prompt.

Now Try This

Show two different methods of working out the following problem:

Rani scored 6 out of 8 in her last maths test. One quarter of her correct answers were for fraction questions. What fraction is this of the total number of questions in the test?

😞 ☑   😐 ☑   😊 ☑

Section Two — Fractions and Ratios

E.g.

Each section is $\frac{1}{32}$.

$\frac{6}{8}$ of whole = $\frac{24}{32}$

Simplified to $\frac{3}{4}$

$\frac{1}{4}$ of $\frac{6}{8}$ = $\frac{6}{32}$

Simplified to $\frac{3}{16}$

OR

$\frac{1}{4}$ × $\frac{6}{8}$ = $\frac{6}{32}$

(simplified to $\frac{3}{16}$)

Showing Greater Depth

Children working at Greater Depth will be able to:

- (Q2) apply their learning to all multiplications of fractions to create a rule or a formula. They should notice that the answer is generated by multiplying the numerators together and then multiplying the denominators together.

Fractions to Decimals

Children need to know that fractions have equivalent decimals and be familiar with those most common. They'll be exploring the relationship between fractions and decimals by using a calculator to find decimal equivalents. They'll learn that some decimals terminate, e.g. $\frac{1}{2} = 0.5$, whereas others recur, e.g. $\frac{1}{3} = 0.3333333\ldots$

Aims:

- Know that the line separating the numerator and denominator means a division calculation.

- Explore how to find equivalent fractions by comparing them to their decimal equivalents.

- Learn the difference between terminating and recurring decimals.

Key Vocabulary:

'numerator', 'denominator', 'recurring', 'terminating'

Resources Needed:

Calculator, pieces of paper (e.g. size A5/A6).

Year 6 Pupil Book — page 20

20

Fractions to Decimals

Warm Up Questions

1) Draw lines to match each fraction to its equivalent decimal.

0.3	$\frac{1}{10}$
0.25	$\frac{1}{5}$
0.6	$\frac{1}{4}$
0.1	$\frac{3}{10}$
0.75	$\frac{3}{5}$
0.2	$\frac{3}{4}$

2) Put these decimal numbers in increasing order of size.

   0.2   0.15   0.302   0.7   0.55   0.099

   0.099   0.15   0.2   0.302   0.55   0.7

(1)
- Choose a fraction $\frac{a}{b}$ where both a and b are whole numbers less than or including 30.
- Perform the calculation on a calculator and write down the decimal answer.

   E.g. fraction: $\frac{2}{9}$

   $2 \div 9 = 0.22222222\ldots$

When a number after the decimal point is repeated forever like 0.222222..., it can be written $0.\dot{2}$. This is called a recurring decimal.

Write your fraction and its equivalent decimal below. If the number has a never-ending string of digits after the decimal point, write all the digits that your calculator shows, followed by '...', or use a dot to show a recurring decimal.

Answers will vary. E.g.

Fraction: $\frac{3}{17}$ Decimal: 0.176470588...

Section Two — Fractions and Ratios

Extra Support

Using a process of elimination is a good idea if any child is unsure of these.

Extra Support

For children who struggle, encourage them to draw a place value chart (a table showing ones, tenths, etc.) to compare digits to the right of the decimal point.

- At this stage, answers should be written exactly as they appear on the calculator (without rounding), followed by a '...' if applicable, although rounding could be suggested as a further challenge later on in the investigation.

- Explain to pupils that the numerator, a, can be smaller or larger than b. Both variations can create a decimal number (unless the numerator is divisible by the denominator), but when the numerator is bigger, the decimal number will include a whole number.

Fractions to Decimals

21

② Repeat the steps of question 1 a few more times using different numerators and denominators each time.

Answers will vary.

Fraction	Decimal
E.g. $\frac{4}{13}$	0.307692307...

Encourage pupils to vary the denominator of each fraction they choose and vary whether the numerator is smaller or bigger than the denominator.

Hand out scrap paper for this — they don't need full sheets of paper, just halves or quarters of A4 sheets will do.

③ Write each decimal you have on a separate piece of paper (big so everyone can see it). Share your decimals with others in the class.
- Does anyone have the same decimal number as you?
- What fraction did they use to create it?
- Are there others with the same decimal value who used a different fraction to create it?

Write your findings below.

E.g. 0.4 could have come from the following:
$$\frac{2}{5}, \frac{4}{10}, \frac{6}{15}, \frac{8}{20}, \frac{10}{25}, \frac{12}{30}.$$

What do your findings show?

E.g. 0.4 means 4 tenths but from looking at calculations you can see that $\frac{4}{10}$ is equal to $\frac{8}{20}$. Because 0.4 is also made from $\frac{6}{15}, \frac{2}{5}, \frac{10}{25}$ and $\frac{12}{30}$, you can also see that $\frac{4}{10}$ is equal to these fractions too.

Section Two — Fractions and Ratios

- As pupils begin to find others with the same decimal as themselves, they can record which fractions give exactly the same decimal answer.
- Plenty of time should be given for this exploration so that plenty of data is gained.

Extra Challenge

If there is time, pupils could order the decimals within their group or table, or even as a whole class.

Encourage discussion about what the numbers to the right of the decimal point mean.

Fractions to Decimals

Year 6 Pupil Book — page 22

4 Now use the table below to record decimals found by dividing the numerator of a fraction by its denominator.

NUMERATOR

	1	2	3	4	5	6	7	8	9	10
10	10	5	$3.\dot{3}$	2.5	2	$1.\dot{6}$	$1.\dot{4}2857\dot{1}$	1.25	$1.\dot{1}$	1
9	9	4.5	3	2.25	1.8	1.5	$1.\dot{2}8571\dot{4}$	1.125	1	0.9
8	8	4	$2.\dot{6}$	2	1.6	$1.\dot{3}$	$1.\dot{1}4285\dot{7}$	1	$0.\dot{8}$	0.8
7	7	3.5	$2.\dot{3}$	1.75	1.4	$1.1\dot{6}$	1	0.875	$0.\dot{7}$	0.7
6	6	3	2	1.5	1.2	1	$0.\dot{8}5714\dot{2}$	0.75	$0.\dot{6}$	0.6
5	5	2.5	$1.\dot{6}$	1.25	1	$0.8\dot{3}$	$0.\dot{7}1428\dot{5}$	0.625	$0.\dot{5}$	0.5
4	4	2	$1.\dot{3}$	1	0.8	$0.\dot{6}$	$0.\dot{5}7142\dot{8}$	0.5	$0.\dot{4}$	0.4
3	3	1.5	1	0.75	0.6	0.5	$0.\dot{4}2857\dot{1}$	0.375	$0.\dot{3}$	0.3
2	2	1	$0.\dot{6}$	0.5	0.4	$0.\dot{3}$	$0.\dot{2}8571\dot{4}$	0.25	$0.\dot{2}$	0.2
1	1	0.5	$0.\dot{3}$	0.25	0.2	$0.1\dot{6}$	$0.\dot{1}4285\dot{7}$	0.125	$0.\dot{1}$	0.1
÷	1	2	3	4	5	6	7	8	9	10

DENOMINATOR

What patterns can you see in the table?

E.g. numbers in the 3 denominator column all end with .3̇ or .6̇ or are whole numbers. The recurring decimals only occur in numbers where the denominator is 7 or a multiple of 3.

Section Two — Fractions and Ratios

- It is not expected that all pupils will complete every box in the table, but to enable patterns to be seen it is sensible to complete the table in a methodical way (row or column at a time) rather than randomly.

- Encourage pupils to look for and discuss patterns they find, e.g. when 3 is the denominator, the answers are either recurring decimals or whole numbers.

- When 7 is the denominator there is a cycle of numbers which appear repeatedly: 142857142857... This can be shown with two dots above the start and end of the cycle, e.g. $0.\dot{1}42857\dot{7}$. Calculators might not show 2 full cycles of these digits, so this may need explaining to pupils.

- In the '6' column, where only the second digit after the decimal point repeats, there should be one dot above this digit, e.g. 0.1666... = $0.1\dot{6}$.

Extra Support

Less able pupils can ignore the '7' column, and be encouraged to fill in certain squares where they are likely to see a clear pattern, e.g. the '1', '2', '4', '5', '9' and/or '10' columns.

Fractions to Decimals

23

(5) **Find decimal numbers in the table that are the same (you could shade them in the same colour). Record the decimals with their corresponding fractions below.**

$$E.g.\ 1.5 = \frac{6}{4}, \frac{3}{2}, \frac{9}{6}$$

Answers will vary but should be taken from the table.

E.g. $0.75 = \frac{3}{4}, \frac{6}{8}$

By grouping different fractions that give the same decimal equivalent, pupils should recognise that they are finding equivalent fractions.

- Children should have noticed that dividing by 9 always creates recurring decimal answers (apart from when the answer is a whole number).

- Repeating this with numbers larger than 10 should reinforce this e.g. $17 \div 9 = 1.88888...$, $25 \div 9 = 2.77777...$ etc.

- When the denominator becomes 99, the decimal answers show alternating recurring digits, e.g. $1 \div 99 = 0.01010101...$, $17 \div 99 = 0.171717...$

- When the denominator is 999, the answers have 3 alternating recurring digits, e.g. $1 \div 999 = 0.001001...$, $17 \div 999 = 0.017017...$

Now Try This
Explore what happens when you create more fractions with a denominator of 9 and convert them into decimal numbers.
What happens when the denominator is 99?
Record your findings.
What do you think will happen when the denominator is 999?
Convert some numbers with a denominator of 999 into decimals.
Were you correct?

 ☑   ☑ ☺ ☑   Section Two — Fractions and Ratios

E.g. Denominator of 9: $17 \div 9 = 1.88888...$, $25 \div 9 = 2.77777...$
So fractions with a denominator of 9 always seem to have a recurring decimal (except when it's a whole number).

Denominator of 99: $1 \div 99 = 0.01010101...$, $17 \div 99 = 0.171717...$ These have 2 alternating recurring digits. I predict that, for 999, answers will have 3 alternating recurring digits.

Denominator of 999: $1 \div 999 = 0.001001...$, $17 \div 999 = 0.017017...$

Showing Greater Depth

Children working at Greater Depth will be able to:

- (Q3) discuss what the numbers to the right of the decimal point mean in relation to fractions.
- (Now Try This) predict the pattern that will be observed with a denominator of 999, based on those seen with denominators of 9 and 99.

Number Rod Ratios

This investigation introduces the idea of ratio, including the notation ':' meaning 'for every'. Children will use number rods to visually represent ratios and will need to work systematically to find all possible ratios.

Aims:

- Recognise and show ratios in a visual way.

- Use the notation a : b and a : b : c to record ratios.

- Work systematically.

- Use common denominators to help compare ratios.

Key Vocabulary:

'ratio', 'equivalent fractions', 'common denominator'

Resources Needed:

A set of number rods for each pair of children.
Printable number rods available at:
cgpbooks.co.uk/KS2-Maths-Investigations

Year 6 Pupil Book — page 24

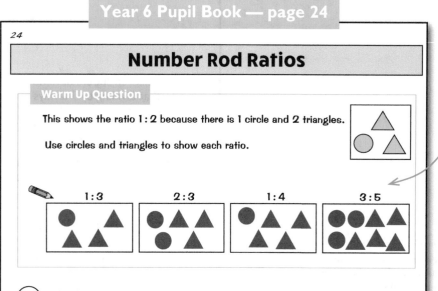

Children may choose to make the first number represent the triangles and the second number represent the circles. This is fine. The number of triangles and the number of circles will be reversed.

- Children should be taught that the reverse ratio 5:3 could be made too. In this case, the gold is still split into 8 parts, but the leprechaun would get the first set of parts (5 parts) and they'd get the second set (3 parts).

- Children could be asked about the proportion of gold they would receive in comparison to the leprechaun. This would encourage them to notice the link between ratio and proportion. They would get $\frac{3}{8}$ of the gold and the leprechaun would get $\frac{5}{8}$ of the gold.

Number Rod Ratios

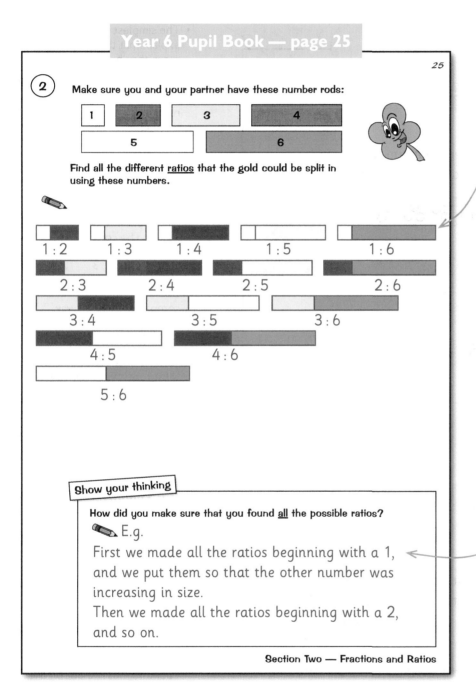

25

(2) Make sure you and your partner have these number rods:

| 1 | 2 | 3 | 4 |

| 5 | 6 |

Find all the different <u>ratios</u> that the gold could be split in using these numbers.

1:2   1:3   1:4   1:5   1:6

2:3   2:4   2:5   2:6

3:4   3:5   3:6

4:5   4:6

5:6

Show your thinking

How did you make sure that you found <u>all</u> the possible ratios?

E.g.
First we made all the ratios beginning with a 1, and we put them so that the other number was increasing in size.
Then we made all the ratios beginning with a 2, and so on.

Section Two — Fractions and Ratios

- All of these ratios can be reversed to put the larger number first, e.g. 6 : 1. The children may consider these different ratios. However, in the context of this investigation, the leprechaun must get more. Therefore, if the ratio represents 'amount of gold you get : amount of gold leprechaun gets', then the smaller number must always go first, and ratios with the larger number first can be disregarded.

- Ratios such as 3 : 3 should be ignored because the leprechaun wouldn't get more than the child.

There are different ways children could be systematic. Here, all the ratios with the white rod first are listed first, then all the ratios with the next largest rod first (red), and so on. Alternatively, children could find all the combinations which make a total of 3, then 4, then 5, etc.

Number Rod Ratios

The ratio 3 : 5 would give more than the ratio 1 : 2. This can be shown in a variety of ways.

- The simplest way would be to explain that the green rod is more than half of the yellow rod ($\frac{3}{5}$ of it) and the white rod is exactly one half of the red rod, therefore 3 : 5 will give them more gold as they're getting more than half of what the leprechaun is getting.

- Alternatively, they may look at the proportions of the whole amount as fractions, then find equivalent fractions so that they can be compared, e.g. $\frac{3}{8} = \frac{9}{24}$ and $\frac{1}{3} = \frac{8}{24}$ so $\frac{3}{8}$ is bigger. They could also convert them to decimals and compare them that way.

- The method shown here is to use trial and error to divide up counters according to the ratios. When they find a number of counters that can be shared exactly in the two ratios, they can compare the numbers of counters in the two smaller portions.

Year 6 Pupil Book — page 26

26

(3) Looking at the ratios **3 : 5** and **1 : 2**, which ratio would give you more of the leprechaun's gold? Show your working below.

You might find it helpful to use counters to represent the pieces of gold.

E.g. Find a number of counters that can be shared in the ratio 3 : 5 and in the ratio 1 : 2.

3 + 5 = 8
6 + 10 = 16
9 + 15 = 24

1 + 2 = 3
2 + 4 = 6
3 + 6 = 9
4 + 8 = 12
5 + 10 = 15
6 + 12 = 18
7 + 14 = 21
8 + 16 = 24

24 counters can be shared out in the two ratios.
I'd get 9 counters from the ratio 3 : 5, or 8 counters from the ratio 1 : 2, so I'd get more gold with the ratio 3 : 5.

Section Two — Fractions and Ratios

Extra Support

- If children struggle to compare the ratios, they could be given 24 counters and directed to count out the pieces of gold they would receive with each ratio.

- They may need help to see that for the ratio 3 : 5, for every 3 counters that are put on the '3' part of the ratio, 5 counters must be put on the second part. In the same way, for every counter put on the first part of the ratio 1 : 2, 2 must be put on the other part.

It is important for the children to realise that the ratio 3 : 5 isn't the better option simply because the 3 (green rod) is bigger than the 1 (white rod). This could be demonstrated by changing the ratio 1 : 2 to 3 : 6.

Number Rod Ratios

27

 (4) In Question 2, you found all the possible ratios using these rods.

| 1 | 2 | 3 | 4 |
| 5 | 6 |

E.g. **Show which ratio will give you the most gold.**

 Ratios where I get more than half of what the leprechaun gets: $2:3$, $3:4$, $3:5$, $4:5$, $4:6$, $5:6$

For $3:4$, I get $\frac{3}{7}$ of the gold, and for $3:5$, I get $\frac{3}{8}$ of the gold. $\frac{3}{7} > \frac{3}{8}$, so $3:4$ gives me more gold.

For $4:5$, I get $\frac{4}{9}$ of the gold.

$3:4 \rightarrow \frac{3}{7} = \frac{27}{63}$ $4:5 \rightarrow \frac{4}{9} = \frac{28}{63}$ so $4:5$ gives me more gold.

For $5:6$, I get $\frac{5}{11}$ of the gold.

$4:5 \rightarrow \frac{4}{9} = \frac{44}{99}$ $5:6 \rightarrow \frac{5}{11} = \frac{45}{99}$ so $5:6$ gives me more gold.

For $4:6$, I get $\frac{4}{10} = \frac{2}{5}$ of the gold (this is the same ratio as $2:3$).

$4:6 \rightarrow \frac{2}{5} = \frac{22}{55}$ $5:6 \rightarrow \frac{5}{11} = \frac{25}{55}$ so $5:6$ gives me more gold.

So the ratio that gives me the most gold is $5:6$.

> Just as you've worked out the best ratio, the leprechaun's twin brother arrives and says he wants a share too. The first leprechaun will still get more than you, but his twin brother will get less than you.
>
> Using the rods from this page, which ratio should the gold be divided into so that you get the largest amount possible?
>
> Following the same rules, which ratio would the leprechaun's twin want the gold to be split into?

  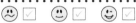   Section Two — Fractions and Ratios

- One way to compare the ratios is to first turn them into fractions. To get the denominator, both the numbers in the ratio must be added.

- The fractions can then be compared like any other fractions — by converting one or both of them to equivalent fractions by making the denominators the same.

- Some children might make the mistake of writing the ratio $2:3$ as the fraction $\frac{2}{3}$ instead of $\frac{2}{5}$.

Extra Support

- If children struggle to convert the ratios to fractions, encourage them to make a table with columns labelled 'ratio', 'number of parts', 'fraction I'll get'.

- This table should give them the chance to identify some inequalities and equivalences.

Extra Challenge

Children could place all the ratios in order of most favourable to least favourable.

After a lot of comparisons, they should find that the order is:

$5:6$, $4:5$, $3:4$, $4:6 = 2:3$, $3:5$, $3:6 = 2:4 = 1:2$, $2:5$, $2:6 = 1:3$, $1:4$, $1:5$, $1:6$

To give me the largest amount possible, the twin brother must get the smallest share possible. So the gold must be split in the ratio $5:6:1$ (where I'll get 5 parts).

The twin brother would want a large share, but it must still be smaller than the other two shares, so it will be $5:6:4$ (where he'll get 4 parts).

Showing Greater Depth

Children working at Greater Depth will be able to:

- (Q4) notice patterns in the ratios to reduce the number of ratios they need to compare (e.g. ruling out those which mean that they get only half as much as the leprechaun).

- (Now Try This) apply what they have discovered in Q4 to three-part ratios (e.g. that they should still get 5 parts of the gold to the leprechaun's 6 parts).

Four Quadrants

In this investigation, children will draw shapes by plotting the coordinate points of their vertices. Children will then apply rules to change the coordinates of the vertices, then analyse the resulting shapes to identify the transformations that have taken place. Transformations will be limited to reflections and translations.

Aims:

- Plot points on the full coordinate grid.
- Apply rules to pairs of coordinates.
- Identify and describe reflections and translations.

Key Vocabulary:

'coordinate', 'quadrant', 'transformation', 'reflection', 'translation', 'axis', 'maps'

Resources Needed:

Rulers
Printable blank coordinate grids
are available at

cgpbooks.co.uk/KS2-Maths-Investigations

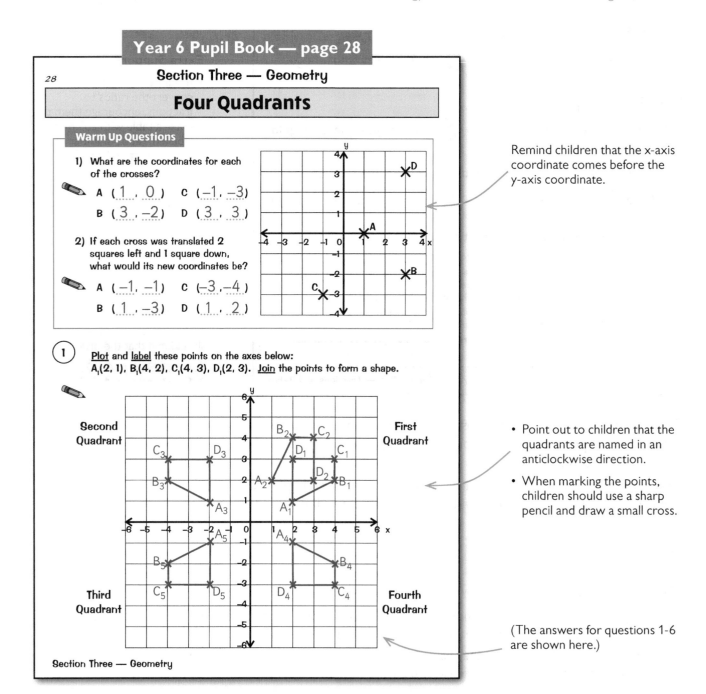

Year 6 Pupil Book — page 28

28   Section Three — Geometry

Four Quadrants

Warm Up Questions

1) What are the coordinates for each of the crosses?

A (1 , 0)   C (−1 , −3)
B (3 , −2)   D (3 , 3)

2) If each cross was translated 2 squares left and 1 square down, what would its new coordinates be?

A (−1 , −1)   C (−3 , −4)
B (1 , −3)   D (1 , 2)

Remind children that the x-axis coordinate comes before the y-axis coordinate.

1) Plot and label these points on the axes below:
A_1(2, 1), B_1(4, 2), C_1(4, 3), D_1(2, 3). Join the points to form a shape.

Second Quadrant

First Quadrant

Third Quadrant

Fourth Quadrant

- Point out to children that the quadrants are named in an anticlockwise direction.
- When marking the points, children should use a sharp pencil and draw a small cross.

(The answers for questions 1-6 are shown here.)

Section Three — Geometry

Four Quadrants

29

(2) Now <u>reverse</u> each pair of coordinates so $A_1(2, 1)$ changes to $A_2(1, 2)$, and so on. Write the new coordinates below.

$A_2(\ 1\ ,\ 2\ )$ $B_2(\ 2\ ,\ 4\ )$ $C_2(\ 3\ ,\ 4\ )$ $D_2(\ 3\ ,\ 2\ )$

Plot and label the points on the grid. Join them to form a second shape. Describe the <u>transformation</u> that maps the first shape onto the second.

A reflection in a diagonal
line that runs from bottom left
to top right.

Think about whether the shape has been reflected across a line or translated ('slid') around the grid.

(3) You're going to change the coordinates $A_1(2, 1)$, $B_1(4, 2)$, $C_1(4, 3)$ and $D_1(2, 3)$ again. This time, make each x-value <u>negative</u> and keep each y-value <u>the same</u>. Write the new coordinates below.

$A_3(\ -2,\ 1\ )$ $B_3(\ -4,\ 2\ )$

$C_3(\ -4,\ 3\ )$ $D_3(\ -2,\ 3\ )$

Plot and label the points on the grid. Join them to make a third shape. Describe the transformation that maps the first shape onto the third.

A reflection in the y-axis.

When you describe a reflection, you need to say what line a shape has been reflected in — it'll often be the x- or y-axis.

Section Three — Geometry

- Explain to children that the 'transformation that maps the first shape onto the second' means how the first shape is changed so that it exactly overlays the second shape. Each point in the original shape must overlay the corresponding point in the second shape, e.g. A_1 must be moved to the same place as A_2.

- A reflection in the line $y = x$ maps the first shape onto the second. The line $y = x$ is the diagonal line where the x- and y-coordinates of the points lying on it are the same, e.g. (1, 1), (2, 2).

- Children may not see the single reflection without help. Ask the questions: 'Is the pattern created by the two shapes symmetrical?' (yes) 'Where is the line of symmetry?' (diagonally through the middle of them)

Children need to realise that the reflected points are the same distance from the mirror line as the original points. E.g. A_1 and A_3 are both 2 units from the y-axis.

Four Quadrants

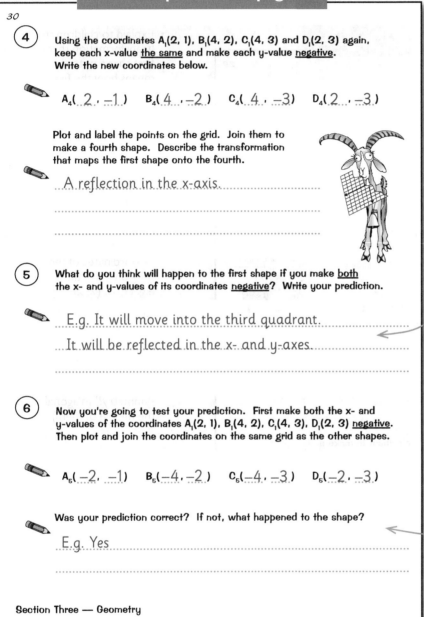

30

④ Using the coordinates $A_1(2, 1)$, $B_1(4, 2)$, $C_1(4, 3)$ and $D_1(2, 3)$ again, keep each x-value <u>the same</u> and make each y-value <u>negative</u>. Write the new coordinates below.

$A_4($ 2 , –1 $)$ $B_4($ 4 , –2 $)$ $C_4($ 4 , –3 $)$ $D_4($ 2 , –3 $)$

Plot and label the points on the grid. Join them to make a fourth shape. Describe the transformation that maps the first shape onto the fourth.

A reflection in the x-axis

⑤ What do you think will happen to the first shape if you make <u>both</u> the x- and y-values of its coordinates <u>negative</u>? Write your prediction.

E.g. It will move into the third quadrant.
It will be reflected in the x- and y-axes

Children may realise that both of the previous transformations are combined to give this transformation.

⑥ Now you're going to test your prediction. First make both the x- and y-values of the coordinates $A_1(2, 1)$, $B_1(4, 2)$, $C_1(4, 3)$, $D_1(2, 3)$ <u>negative</u>. Then plot and join the coordinates on the same grid as the other shapes.

$A_6($–2 , –1 $)$ $B_6($–4 , –2 $)$ $C_6($–4 , –3 $)$ $D_6($–2 , –3 $)$

Was your prediction correct? If not, what happened to the shape?

E.g. Yes

Extra Challenge

Children could trace the first shape and rotate it around. They should notice that a reflection in both axes has the same effect as a rotation of 180° about the point (0, 0).

Section Three — Geometry

Four Quadrants

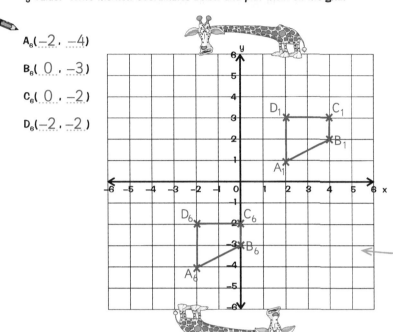

7 On the grid below, plot points A₁(2, 1), B₁(4, 2), C₁(4, 3) and D₁(2, 3) again. Then subtract 4 from each x-value and subtract 5 from each y-value. Write the new coordinates below and plot them on the grid.

A₆(−2 , −4)

B₆(0 , −3)

C₆(0 , −2)

D₆(−2 , −2)

Describe what has happened to the shape.

It has moved 4 squares left and 5 squares down.

It is still the same way up and the same way round.

 Now Try This For this activity, you will need a grid showing all 4 quadrants. With a partner, plot a shape and label it 1. Make up a rule that changes the x- or y-value (or both) of each point. Apply the rule and draw the new shape. Label it 2. Now swap with another pair in your class, and see if you can work out the rule they used to transform their shape.

Section Three — Geometry

Extra Support

Subtracting across zero may pose a challenge for some children. Encourage them to use the axis as a number line.

- The big difference between this transformation and the others is that the shape hasn't changed orientation, or been flipped over. It has simply been slid across the grid, horizontally and vertically.

- This type of transformation is called a translation.

They must identify a pattern that holds for all pairs of coordinates before deciding what the rule was. E.g. if a coordinate changes from 1 to –1, the rule could have been to make it negative, or to subtract 2.

A coordinate grid is provided online for you to print out.

E.g. coordinates of shape 1 = (4, 3), (4, 5), (1, 5).

Rule = make the x-value negative and subtract 1 from the y-value.

Coordinates of shape 2 = (−4, 2), (−4, 4), (−1, 4).

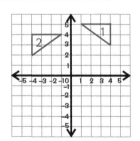

Extra Challenge

Some children could be encouraged to combine two rules, as in the example here.

Showing Greater Depth

Children working at Greater Depth will be able to:

- (Now Try This) analyse the change from the original shape to the new shape, one coordinate at a time.

Key Stage 2 Maths Investigations — Year 6

Algebraic Shapes

In this investigation, children will be using letters to represent lengths. They'll be calculating perimeters of different triangles and quadrilaterals, and using letters to create algebraic equations.

Aims:

- Draw shapes using given criteria.
- Identify 2D shapes.
- Use algebra to express perimeters.

Key Vocabulary:

'triangle', 'quadrilateral', 'perimeter'

Resources Needed:

Rulers

Pegboards and rubber bands are needed for the final challenge. These can be homemade from wood and nails, or a sheet of printable pegboards is available at cgpbooks.co.uk/KS2-Maths-Investigations

Year 6 Pupil Book — page 32

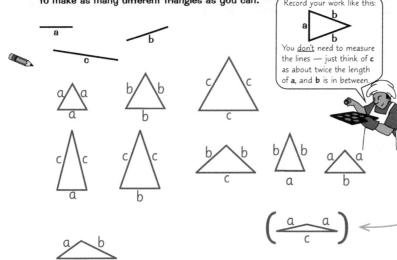

32

Algebraic Shapes

Warm Up Questions

Work out what the letters represent in each of these equations:

a) $7 + u = 56$ $u = 49$

b) $45 \div v = 5$ $v = 9$

c) $w - 7 = -15$ $w = -8$

d) $12 \times x = 4800$ $x = 400$

e) $y + 0.5 = 0.8$ $y = 0.3$

f) $z \div 6 = 0.5$ $z = 3$

(1) Each letter represents a different length side of a triangle. Sides can be short (a), medium (b) or long (c). Use different combinations of lengths to make as many different triangles as you can.

Record your work like this:

You don't need to measure the lines — just think of **c** as about twice the length of **a**, and **b** is in between.

I found 10 triangles in total.

Section Three — Geometry

Children need to use their knowledge of times tables and their inverses to calculate the answers.

Extra Support

$a + a + b$, $b + b + c$ and $a + a + c$ are only viable options if two of the short sides put together come to a length greater than the longer side.

$a + a + c$ is technically not possible with the lines given, because the 'a' lines are too short. However, as pupils were not required to measure the lines, they could have given this answer anyway.

What makes a viable triangle could still be explained. Demonstrate this to the children with strips of paper, e.g. 10 cm, 3 cm and 3 cm. The two shorter sides will not meet if placed at either end of the 10 cm strip, so making a triangle is not possible.

Algebraic Shapes

33

2 You have two copies of the triangle below. The two triangles can be joined together, but the two sides that are joined together must be the same length and must completely join from corner to corner. You cannot reflect the triangle.
How many different shapes can you make? Draw them below and name the shapes you have created.

Be precise with your names.

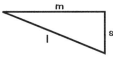

3 possible shapes:

Parallelogram:

Rectangle:

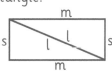

Parallelogram:

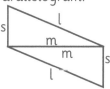

3 If the lengths are labelled s (for shortest side), m (for middle length) and l (for longest side), the <u>perimeter</u> of one triangle is s + m + l.
Look at the shapes you made in Question 2. Write the equations for their perimeters.

Perimeter of parallelogram (where sides s are joined together) = m + l + m + l = 2m + 2l

Perimeter of rectangle = s + m + s + m = 2s + 2m

Perimeter of parallelogram (where sides m are joined together) = s + l + s + l = 2s + 2l

Section Three — Geometry

The shape must remain identical, so rotations of it are allowed, but not reflections. Therefore these shapes are not possible:

Children should recognise that when 2 identical triangles are joined like this, it makes a 4 sided-shape. This is because from a total of 6 sides, 2 of them join and become hidden inside the new shape, leaving only 4 sides for the new outline.

Pupils are likely to write their answers with the individual sides as four separate terms, e.g. m + l + m + l, but more able pupils could be encouraged to collect the terms, e.g. 2m + 2l.

Algebraic Shapes

Year 6 Pupil Book — page 34

Any other variations create congruent shapes. There are only 3 perimeters possible.

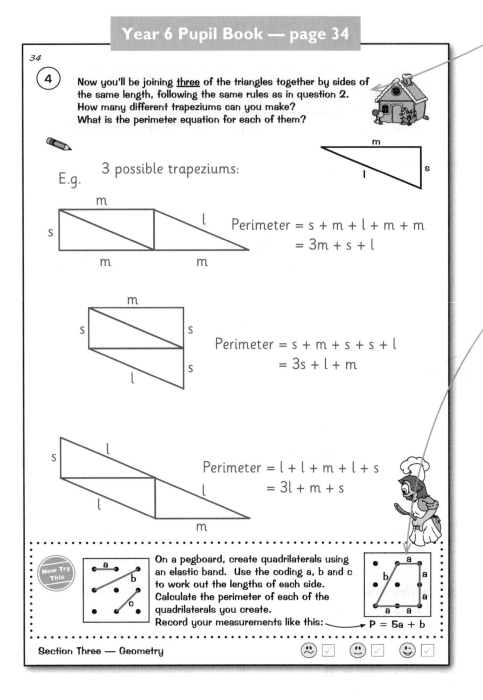

Extra Challenge

Pupils who finish early could explore:

- What happens if four of these shapes are joined together? How do the perimeters and equations alter? What shapes can be made?

Answers will vary but could be any of the following:

P = 8a

P = 4c

P = 3a + b + c

P = 3a + b + c

P = 2b + 2c

P = a + b + 2c

P = 4a

P = 2a + 2c

P = 6a

P = a + b + 2c

P = 2a + 3c

P = 4a + c

P = 2a + 2b

P = 2a + 2b

P = 2a + 2b

Showing Greater Depth

Children working at Greater Depth will be able to:

- (Q1) show systematic thinking by thinking of the order in which they write their combinations. The best way to be systematic is by changing only one side (or letter) at a time.

Key Stage 2 Maths Investigations — Year 6

Volume and Surface Area

In this investigation, pupils will explore how cuboids of the same volume can be made with different dimensions, and how these cuboids can have different surface areas despite having the same volume. Children will also draw their shapes, using isometric dotty paper.

Aims:

- Calculate and compare volumes of cuboids.
- Calculate areas of cuboid faces to find total surface area.
- Draw shapes accurately using isometric paper.

Key Vocabulary:

'product', 'cube', 'cuboid', 'volume', 'surface area', 'face'

Resources Needed:

Ruler, connecting cubes

Isometric dotty paper is available at
cgpbooks.co.uk/KS2-Maths-Investigations

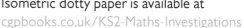

Year 6 Pupil Book — page 35

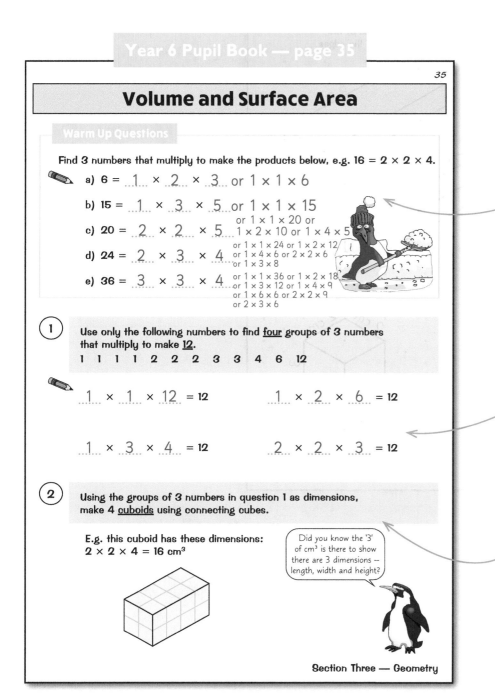

Remind children of the commutative law, so they know $1 \times 2 \times 3 = 1 \times 3 \times 2$ or $2 \times 3 \times 1$ etc.

This can be done systematically by beginning with the smallest numbers or the largest numbers and working in order of size.

- Encourage children to begin constructing cuboids by making the length first, then create a rectangle by adding width to it. Finally add height to the rectangle they have made.

- For images of the cuboids that pupils should be making here, see the answers on the next page.

Volume and Surface Area

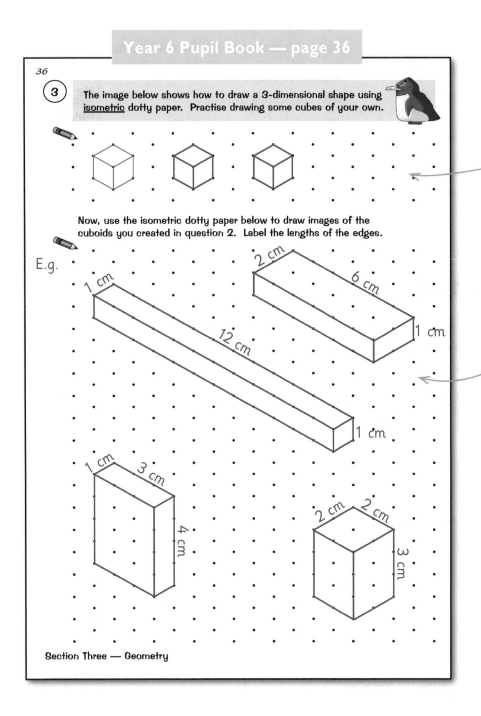

36

3 The image below shows how to draw a 3-dimensional shape using <u>isometric</u> dotty paper. Practise drawing some cubes of your own.

Now, use the isometric dotty paper below to draw images of the cuboids you created in question 2. Label the lengths of the edges.

E.g.

1 cm

12 cm

1 cm

2 cm

6 cm

1 cm

1 cm

1 cm

3 cm

4 cm

2 cm

2 cm

3 cm

Section Three — Geometry

Opposite lines need to be drawn parallel to each other.

Drawings may look different, depending on which way round pupils have drawn their cuboids.

Volume and Surface Area

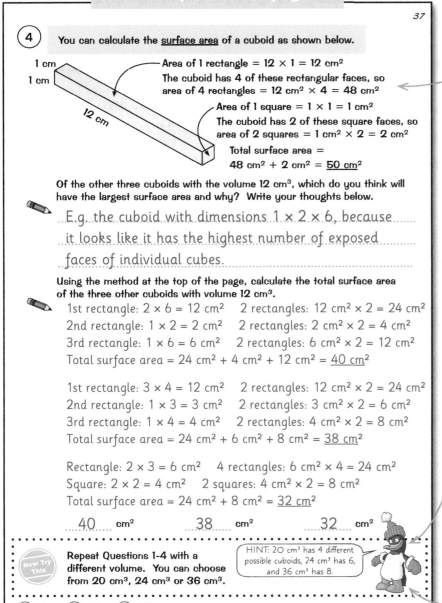

37

4 You can calculate the surface area of a cuboid as shown below.

1 cm
1 cm
12 cm

Area of 1 rectangle = 12 × 1 = 12 cm²
The cuboid has 4 of these rectangular faces, so area of 4 rectangles = 12 cm² × 4 = 48 cm²

Area of 1 square = 1 × 1 = 1 cm²
The cuboid has 2 of these square faces, so area of 2 squares = 1 cm² × 2 = 2 cm²

Total surface area = 48 cm² + 2 cm² = 50 cm²

Of the other three cuboids with the volume 12 cm³, which do you think will have the largest surface area and why? Write your thoughts below.

E.g. the cuboid with dimensions 1 × 2 × 6, because it looks like it has the highest number of exposed faces of individual cubes.

Using the method at the top of the page, calculate the total surface area of the three other cuboids with volume 12 cm³.

1st rectangle: 2 × 6 = 12 cm²   2 rectangles: 12 cm² × 2 = 24 cm²
2nd rectangle: 1 × 2 = 2 cm²   2 rectangles: 2 cm² × 2 = 4 cm²
3rd rectangle: 1 × 6 = 6 cm²   2 rectangles: 6 cm² × 2 = 12 cm²
Total surface area = 24 cm² + 4 cm² + 12 cm² = 40 cm²

1st rectangle: 3 × 4 = 12 cm²   2 rectangles: 12 cm² × 2 = 24 cm²
2nd rectangle: 1 × 3 = 3 cm²   2 rectangles: 3 cm² × 2 = 6 cm²
3rd rectangle: 1 × 4 = 4 cm²   2 rectangles: 4 cm² × 2 = 8 cm²
Total surface area = 24 cm² + 6 cm² + 8 cm² = 38 cm²

Rectangle: 2 × 3 = 6 cm²   4 rectangles: 6 cm² × 4 = 24 cm²
Square: 2 × 2 = 4 cm²   2 squares: 4 cm² × 2 = 8 cm²
Total surface area = 24 cm² + 8 cm² = 32 cm²

40 cm²   38 cm²   32 cm²

Now Try This

Repeat Questions 1-4 with a different volume. You can choose from 20 cm³, 24 cm³ or 36 cm³.

HINT: 20 cm³ has 4 different possible cuboids, 24 cm³ has 6, and 36 cm³ has 8.

Section Three — Geometry

You can explain to pupils what surface area is as "the sum of the areas of the exposed faces of the shape".

20 cm³:

20 × 1 × 1   10 × 2 × 1
5 × 4 × 1   5 × 2 × 2

24 cm³:

24 × 1 × 1   12 × 2 × 1
8 × 3 × 1   6 × 4 × 1
6 × 2 × 2   4 × 3 × 2

36 cm³:

36 × 1 × 1   18 × 2 × 1
12 × 3 × 1   9 × 4 × 1
6 × 6 × 1   9 × 2 × 2
6 × 3 × 2   4 × 3 × 3

Encourage children to predict which cuboid will have the largest surface area, to see if there is a similarity with previous answers.

- Examples should be given, e.g. 13 cm³ = 13 × 1 × 1 and 19 cm³ = 19 × 1 × 1

- Children should soon recognise that prime numbers can't be factorised and therefore there are no alternative dimensions. Therefore there is only ever one possible surface area.

Extra Challenge

For Greater Depth, pupils could be provided with the following question: Madame Mathematician says that when the volume of a cuboid is a prime number, and the side lengths are all whole numbers, there will only be one set of dimensions possible and therefore only one possible surface area. Do you agree? Show your thinking with examples.

Showing Greater Depth

Children working at Greater Depth will be able to:

- (Q4) predict which cuboid will give the largest surface area by analysing the sizes of the cuboids they have made and the dimensions they have. They'll recognise that because the surface area is the sum of the exposed faces of the individual connecting cubes, the cuboid with the largest surface area will have the fewest connecting cube faces hidden 'inside' the cuboid.

How Old Am I?

Children need to know the months of the year and how many days each month has. They'll also need to understand how leap years work. Children will be calculating their ages in years, months and days, and then using facts about time to calculate their age to the nearest month, week, day, hour and minute. They'll be working with large numbers up to ten million.

Aims:

- Read and write numbers up to ten million.

- Round numbers to a required degree of accuracy.

- Solve number and practical problems using large numbers.

Key Vocabulary:

'years', 'months', 'weeks', 'days', 'hours', 'minutes', 'leap years'

Resources Needed:

Calculator.

Year 6 Pupil Book — page 38

38
Section Four — Measurement and Statistics

How Old Am I?

Warm Up Questions

How many days are there in each month of the year?

January: 31	May: 31	September: 30
February: 28 or 29	June: 30	October: 31
March: 31	July: 31	November: 30
April: 30	August: 31	December: 31

How is February different from the other months?

February has two possible answers because it usually has 28 days, but every 4 years it has 29 days.

(1) On what date were you born? Calculate exactly how old you are in <u>years</u>, <u>months</u> and <u>days</u>.

Answers will vary.

I am _____ years, _____ months and _____ days old.

(2) Now use your workings from question 1 to calculate how old you are in <u>months</u>, to the nearest month.

Answers will vary. E.g. a pupil exactly 11 years old will be 132 months old.

I am _____ months old.

Section Four — Measurement and Statistics

Extra Support

Pupils who can't remember how many days are in each month can be reminded of the rhyme:

30 days has September,
April, June and November.
All the rest have 31,
Except for February alone,
Which has 28 days clear,
And 29 in each leap year.

- It is important that pupils know that a 29-day February occurs every 4 years, and leap years are divisible by 4, e.g. 2000, 2004, 2008, 2012 etc.

- Pupils can be reminded that we have leap years because it takes the Earth $365\frac{1}{4}$ days to orbit the Sun, so every four years there's an extra day.

There are websites that calculate age in years, months, etc. if you enter a birth date — one of these could be used to let children check their answers throughout this investigation.

To calculate this answer:

- multiply the number of complete years by 12.

- add the number of complete months.

- round the remaining days up if over half a month or ignoring remaining days if under half a month.

How Old Am I?

Year 6 Pupil Book — page 39

39

(3) Next, work out how many <u>days</u> old you are.
(Don't forget about leap years!)

Answers will vary, but, assuming children are of a similar age,
partners will be able to calculate the 'bulk' of their age together, e.g.:

If the investigation is being done in 2023, pupils born in
2012 can work out:

2013 (365 days) + 2014 (365 days) + 2015 (365 days) +
2016 (366 days) + 2017 (365 days) + 2018 (365 days) +
2019 (365 days) + 2020 (366 days) + 2021 (365 days) +
2022 (365 days) + days in 2023 so far.

The year 2012 was a leap year — they happen every 4 years.

At this stage, partners are on an identical number
of days. They now need to calculate how many
days from their birth date to the end of 2012.

I am .... days old.

Answers are likely to be in the
area of around 4000 days for
10-11 year-olds.

(4) Using your answer to question 3, work out how old are you in <u>weeks</u>,
to the nearest week.

Answers will vary. E.g. a pupil exactly
11 years old will be 4018 days old,
which is 574 weeks old.

The answer to this will be
calculated by:

• dividing the number of days
by 7.

• rounding up to one more week
if the remainder is 4 or more,
or ignoring it if it's 3 or fewer.

I am .... weeks old.

Section Four — Measurement and Statistics

How Old Am I?

There are some issues that will make this question more complicated:

- Pupils born in a different time zone who know the time they were born will have to convert it to UK time.

- Ignoring daylight saving time may make hours one hour out.

Answer to age to the nearest hour will be calculated by:

- subtracting one day from their total age in days and replacing it with the number of hours (and minutes) that passed after their time of birth on their birth date (11 hours if using 1 pm),

- multiplying age in full days by 24,

- adding the number of hours and minutes that have already passed today

- Add together any minutes from the day of birth and the present day — if they come to 30 or over, round up to an additional hour, and if they're under 30, ignore them.

Year 6 Pupil Book — page 40

40

(5) 1 day = 24 hours   1 hour = 60 minutes
Using this knowledge, calculate the answers to the following questions.
If you don't know what time you were born at, imagine you were born at exactly 1 o'clock in the afternoon.

How old are you in hours, to the nearest hour?

Answers will vary, and will reach the high tens of thousands or over 100 000.

Don't forget to include how many hours have passed today, and how many hours passed after your birth on the day you were born.

I am .... hours old.

How old are you in minutes, to the nearest minute?

Answers will vary, and will reach into the millions.

The challenge with finding how many minutes old you are is that your answer will keep changing as you calculate it.

The good news is you're allowed to use a calculator!

I am .... minutes old.

 Now Try This Work with a group. Write the age in minutes that you calculated onto a piece of paper. Take turns in reading them out, then get yourself into order from youngest to oldest. What is your total age in minutes? By how many minutes is the oldest person older than the youngest person?

Section Four — Measurement and Statistics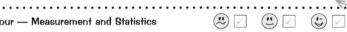

Answer to age to the nearest minute will be calculated by:

- multiplying age in hours by 60,

- then adding the number of minutes that have already passed that hour (and any extra minutes from the day of birth).

When reading large numbers out loud, it is important to remind children to group the thousand numbers together, e.g. 4 567 323 = four million, five hundred and sixty-seven thousand, three hundred and twenty-three. A common error is to say four million, five hundred thousand, sixty-seven thousand etc. When calculating with large numbers, ensure place value columns are used for accuracy.

Showing Greater Depth

Children working at Greater Depth will be able to:

- (Q2-5) recognise what to do with the remainders in these calculations, e.g. understand how to work out what should be rounded up or down, and know how the answers could also be given as whole numbers with a remainder in the next smallest time unit.

Stars and Statistics

In this investigation, children will be collecting data and calculating the range, mode, median and mean of their data. They'll compare the different averages and how well they reflect the data set. Before tackling this investigation, children should be familiar with finding the mean of a data set.

Aims:

- Make a sensible estimate of a quantity.
- Systematically record a set of data.
- Find different averages and the range.

Key Vocabulary:

'average', 'estimate', 'range', 'mean', 'mode', 'median'

Resources Needed:

Calculator. Page of stars available at cgpbooks.co.uk/KS2-Maths-Investigations

---

Year 6 Pupil Book — page 41

41

Stars and Statistics

Warm Up Questions

The <u>mean</u> (average) is found by <u>adding</u> all the numbers in a group and <u>dividing</u> by how many numbers there are. Find the mean of the numbers in each circle:

$35 \div 7 = 5$ $104 \div 8 = 13$ $250 \div 5 = 50$

---

① Your teacher will show you an image of some stars for about 5 seconds. How many stars do you think you saw? Write your <u>estimate</u> in the star below.

E.g.

25

Your teacher will now collect together all the estimates from the class. <u>Record</u> them all in the space below.

Think about how you could be systematic in recording the estimates. E.g. you might put them in order.

20	30	37	40	50	80
25	31	39	40	51	
27	35		40		
29	35		42		
29	36		44		

② Find the <u>range</u> of the estimates. The range is the <u>difference</u> between the <u>minimum</u> and <u>maximum</u> values.

E.g. $80 - 20 = 60$

Section Four — Measurement and Statistics

- A sheet of stars is provided online. It can either be printed or shown on a screen. Alternatively, you can draw simple stars on a sheet of paper. The exact number isn't important, but it should be too many for the children to count in 5 seconds.

- Encourage children not to try to count the stars individually but to imagine them in groups.

Discuss with the class a suitable way of recording the estimates. For example, a tally chart would be good if many children chose the same values. Here, they've been placed in groups with a common tens digit.

Stars and Statistics

42

(3) How could you work out a <u>class estimate</u> for the number of stars?

Show your thinking

Discuss your ideas with a partner and write them below.

 E.g.
We could find the mean by adding all the estimates and dividing the total by the number of children in the class.

Other suggestions might be to:

- use the most popular estimate.
- use the value halfway between the minimum estimate and the maximum estimate.

Remind children that the purpose of this activity is not to establish the correct answer but to find a number that reflects fairly the thoughts of the class as a group.

(4) You are now going to find the <u>mode</u>, <u>median</u> and <u>mean</u> for the estimates.
The mode is the value that the largest number of people said.
The median is the middle value when you put all the numbers in order.

E.g.

 Mode 40

Median 20, 25, 27, 29, 29, 30, 31, 35, 35, 36, 37, 39, 40, 40, 40, 42, 44, 50, 51, 80

Median = 36.5

The MOde is the MOst popular.

The MEDian is like the MEDium. It might fall halfway between two values.

Mean

20 + 25 + 27 + 29 + 29 + 30 + 31 + 35 + 35 + 36 + 37 + 39 + 40 + 40 + 40 + 42 + 44 + 50 + 51 + 80 = 760

760 ÷ 20 = 38

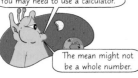

Hmm... so many numbers... You may need to use a calculator.

The mean might not be a whole number.

Section Four — Measurement and Statistics

- Pupils may need to be taught the terms 'mode' and 'median' in more detail to be able to answer this question.
- There may not be a mode, or there might be more than one mode.
- To find the median, children need to write the numbers out in order from smallest to largest. In this example, there are 20 numbers, so the median is halfway between the 10th and 11th numbers.

Extra Support

- To reduce the number of values that children need to add, portions of the data set could be allocated to pairs of children, or the class could be divided into smaller groups.
- Alternatively, the estimates could be input into a spreadsheet and the total found.

It is likely the mean will not be a whole number. Encourage children to discuss how best to represent this number (e.g. by rounding it to the nearest whole number).

Stars and Statistics

43

Show your thinking

Do you think the mean, mode or median is the <u>best class estimate</u>? Explain why.

✏ Answers will vary, e.g.

I think the mode is the best estimate, because it isn't affected by the extremely high value. / I think the median is the best estimate, because it's in the mid-30s, and a lot of people guessed a number in the 30s.

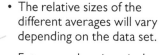

(5) Now you know the class averages, you might want to change your estimate. Write your <u>new estimate</u> in the star.

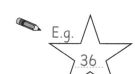

E.g.

★ 36

Your teacher will now collect together all the new estimates from the class. Record them all in the space below.

27	30	35	40
29	30	36	40
29	30	36	42
	33	36	45
	34	37	
	35	39	
	35		

(6) Find the <u>range</u> of the new estimates.

✏ E.g. 45 − 27 = 18

Section Four — Measurement and Statistics

- The relative sizes of the different averages will vary depending on the data set.

- Extreme values in a single direction will affect the mean, but may not affect the mode or median.

- If the mean, mode and median are all very similar, children can say that any of them will do.

- This second estimate is intended to be made considering the findings of the first estimate, and so the stars do not need to be shown again.

- There may be fewer different values for the second estimates, so a different recording system, e.g. tally chart, may be appropriate.

Stars and Statistics

44

Show your thinking

Is the range of this set of estimates different from the range of the first set of estimates? Why do you think this is?

E.g.

The range was much smaller in the second set because people who had originally made very high or low estimates changed them.

> Answers will vary but it is expected that the range of values will be smaller for the second estimate, with more values closer to the mean from the first estimate.

(7) Now find the mode, median and mean for the new estimates.

E.g.

Mode Three modes, 30, 35 and 36

Median 27, 29, 29, 30, 30, 30, 33, 34, 35, 35, 35, 36, 36, 36, 37, 39, 40, 40, 42, 45

median = 35

Mean 27 + 29 + 29 + 30 + 30 + 30 + 33 + 34 + 35 + 35 + 35 + 36 + 36 + 36 + 37 + 39 + 40 + 40 + 42 + 45 = 698

698 ÷ 20 = 34.9

> On the provided sheet there were 32 stars. It will be interesting to look at whether the averages became closer to the actual answer on the second estimate.

(8) Your teacher will now reveal how many stars there really were.

Write down the difference between the number of real stars and the estimate you wrote in Question 5.

E.g. 36 − 32 = 4

Now Try This A set of 5 values has a mode of 6, a median of 6 and a mean of 7. Suggest what the values might be. Can you think of any different answers?

Section Four — Measurement and Statistics

Mode = 6, so at least 2 values must be 6.

The median is 6, so there must be a 6 in the middle.   6?   6   6? ......

The mean is 7, so the total = 5 × 7 = 35.

If there are three 6s, 3 × 6 = 18, the other two numbers must add to 35 − 18 = 17. One must be the smallest number in the set and the other must be the biggest. The numbers could be 1, 6, 6, 6, 16.

Other sets include: 2, 6, 6, 6, 15; 3, 6, 6, 6, 14; 4, 6, 6, 6, 13; 5, 6, 6, 6, 12; 6, 6, 6, 6, 11.

There are lots more possible data sets with just two 6s. It is also possible to get more answers with three sixes, if you allow negative numbers and zero. An infinite number of answers are possible if non-integers are allowed.

Showing Greater Depth

Children working at Greater Depth will be able to:

- (Q4) justify their choice of which average represents the data set best, for example by referring to the effect of extreme values.